ROCKETS & MISSILES

No product of science and technology has advanced more rapidly than the rocket. Today, with astronauts journeying to the Moon every few months, it is difficult to believe that in the mid-1950's there were many highly respected engineers who predicted failure for American and Soviet plans to put small scientific satellites into orbit around the Earth. Their scepticism was dispelled on October 4, 1957 when radio stations all over the world relayed the 'bleeps' received from Sputnik 1.

It had taken some seven centuries to progress from the primitive firework rockets of the Chinese to the modest triumph of the first artificial satellite. Less than four years later a man orbited the Earth. Within eight more years men had reached the Moon, photographed Mars automatically and parachuted instruments on to the surface of Venus.

This book traces the story of the rocket throughout its 700-year recorded history. It tells how the simple firework has evolved into a vehicle capable of annihilating mankind in his own world or of carrying him to new worlds far out in space.

A
GROSSET
ALL-COLOR GUIDE

ROCKETS & MISSILES

BY JOHN W. R. TAYLOR
Illustrated by Gordon Davies

GROSSET & DUNLAP
A NATIONAL GENERAL COMPANY
Publishers • New York

CONTENTS

4   History of the rocket

28   Control and guidance of missiles

78   Rockets into space

92   Men into space

110 Reaching for the Moon

134 Experiments for the future

156 Books to read

157 Index

HISTORY OF THE ROCKET

The first rockets

In the year A.D. 994 the city of Tzu T'ung in China was besieged by an army of 100,000 men. The inhabitants were alarmed when the enemy finally launched a fierce frontal attack, but the commander of the defense forces, Chang Yung, called his artillery into action. So heavy was the barrage of stones, hurled from catapults, and fire-arrows that the enemy beat a hurried retreat.

We shall never know if the fire-arrows used at Tzu T'ung, and in earlier battles, were rockets or merely arrows tipped with inflammable material; but genuine rockets, propelled by black powder (later known as gunpowder), were in widespread use by the thirteenth century. Their effect was psychological as well as destructive, for one writer recorded that when lit they made a thunderous noise that seemed to make the heavens shake.

This may sound an extravagant claim for rockets that consisted of a tube of black powder tied to an arrow, with occasional refinements such as a coating of poison over the tip; but design progress was rapid.

The tube of black powder became longer and was given a pointed nose that dispensed with the need for an arrowhead.

4

When it was discovered that fire-arrows would still fly a straight course after the feathers of the arrow had been burned away by the rocket exhaust, the feathers were also dropped, leaving a missile similar in shape to a firework rocket.

Weapons of this kind were fired by the Chinese in salvoes, from cylinders or boxes that housed up to a hundred rounds.

How a rocket works

Rockets work on the principle expressed in Sir Isaac Newton's Third Law of Motion: 'To every action there is an equal and opposite reaction'. The air inside a balloon exerts an equal force in every direction, giving it a spherical shape. If we untie the neck, the air escapes downward. The same force with which it pushes through the neck is exerted against the inside of the balloon in the opposite direction (Newton's 'reaction'), so that the balloon flies upward if released. When gunpowder is burned inside a firework rocket, the hot gases that are produced work in the same way, propelling it in a direction opposite to that of the escaping exhaust gases.

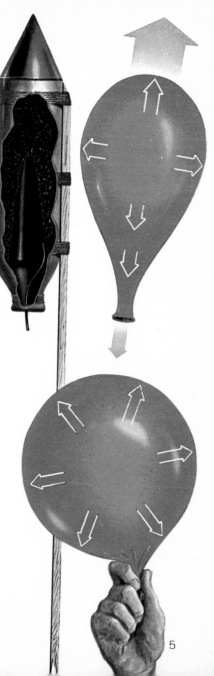

The rocket principle can be demonstrated with a toy balloon.

5

Naval rockets in action.

The Rocket's Red Glare

It did not take other nations long to copy the early types of rocket invented by the Chinese. Having learned the effectiveness of such weapons from the receiving end, the Mongols used them during their capture of Baghdad in 1258. The Arabs, in turn, adopted the weapons that had contributed to their defeat and fired them against French troops led by King Louis IX during the Seventh Crusade.

Before long the French themselves were setting the pace in military rocketry. They used rockets in the defense of Orleans in 1429, when Joan of Arc achieved her great victory, and in many subsequent campaigns; but with the development of cannon and small arms the less accurate rocket gradually fell out of favor.

Its rebirth seems to have followed the battles of Seringapatam, in India, in 1792 and 1799. On the first occasion, Tippoo Sahib launched a tremendous rocket barrage against the British army as a prelude to an assault by six thousand of his picked troops. One observer reported that they were more noisy than dangerous; but a young officer wrote:

6

'Every illumination of blue lights (from air-bursting rockets) was accompanied by a shower of rockets, some of which entered the head of the column, passing through to the rear, causing death, wounds and dreadful lacerations from the long bamboos which are attached to them.'

One of Tippoo's rockets, which can be seen in the Royal Artillery Museum in London, is bound to a forty-inch sword blade, which would help to explain the lacerations mentioned above. The rocket itself is fairly crude, with an iron case ten inches long and two and a half inches in diameter. It had a range of about a thousand yards.

By 1804, at Woolwich Arsenal, Colonel (later Sir) William Congreve had refined these crude missiles into larger, long-range military rockets, carried by specially-modified ships. More than two thousand 32-pounders were launched against Boulogne in 1806, so shattering the French that not a shot was fired in return. In the following year, Copenhagen suffered great damage from fire when 25,000 Congreve incendiary rockets descended upon it.

A similar barrage was used by the British against the United States in the War of 1812. Rockets were fired against Fort McHenry in Baltimore by the British sloop *Erebus*. This occasion inspired Francis Scott Key to write the words to "The Star-Spangled Banner."

The rocket-ship *Erebus* bombarding Fort McHenry, Baltimore, during the War of 1812.

Explosive Payload

Fin
Stabilized
Rocket

Spin
Stabilized
Rocket

Rear end showing Vanes
designed to spin Rocket

Nineteenth-century war rockets

The rockets developed by Congreve were a great improvement over their predecessors. Examples now in the Royal Artillery Museum in England range in weight from 18 to 300 pounds; but those used at Boulogne and Copenhagen, and in the War of 1812, averaged about 32 pounds. The gunpowder charge was contained in an iron casing 3 feet 6 inches long and 4 inches in diameter, mounted on a 15-foot stick. Such a weapon had a range of 3,000 yards and was very cheap to produce.

The most effective warhead for use against towns, forts and ships was a conical metal type which embedded itself in the target and then oozed a slow-burning incendiary mixture. This type of rocket was carried in some twenty batteries on the *Erebus*, each battery consisting of a box housing a number of metal firing tubes.

The second type of Congreve rocket contained shot

Typical 19th-century combat rocket (*top*). The later and more accurate Frezier (*center*) and Hale rockets.

which was ejected like shrapnel by an explosive gunpowder charge. It was produced in a variety of sizes, the smallest being 3- to 12-pounders carried and fired from a prone position by infantry.

A British rocket brigade, including mounted units, took part in the Battle of Waterloo in 1815. But Congreve's rockets achieved their greatest successes in America in 1812–14. Some American ships were sunk, but it was morale that suffered most. Describing the rout of General William Pinkney's rifle batallion by a British rocket squad on August 24, 1814, the British commander commented: 'Never did men with arms in their hands make better use of their legs.'

The drawback of all rockets built up to this time was their inaccuracy. A Frenchman named Frezier suggested the use of dart-type stabilizing fins, but the real answer was to make the rocket spin in the way that a bullet is spun by the rifling in a gun-barrel.

An Englishman named William Hale found the answer in a combination of canted tail-fins and a ring of small secondary nozzles through which some of the exhaust gases could be ejected to spin-stabilize his rockets. By the mid-nineteenth century Hale rockets were standard equipment in the British and American armies and were used most effectively in the Mexican War in 1847.

Austrian troops firing stick rockets.

Life-saving rockets

Reference has been made to Tippoo Sahib's use of rockets which burst in the air. Congreve improved on this idea by fitting parachutes to some of his flare-rockets so that they could illuminate a battlefield for a prolonged period as they floated down. Such devices were refinements of the firework and signal rockets that had been used in the Far East nearly as long as war rockets.

Many attempts had been made to transport messages or small packages by rocket, but the inaccuracy of the stick rocket was not improved by the payload, which was often deposited in the wrong hands. Not until 1807 was anything practical achieved. In that year, an Englishman named Henry Trengrouse fastened a light cord to a rocket and devised a new way of carrying a lifeline to a ship in distress. By hauling in the cord draped over their vessel by the rocket, shipwrecked sailors were able to drag over a heavier rope tied to its end and then clamber along this to safety.

Invention of the multistage rocket

The next step was to find ways of improving the power and range of rockets, to bring help to ships at greater distances from the shore.

Once again, the basic idea came from Frezier. He suggested putting rockets one behind the other, so that as the first burned itself out it would ignite the one right in front of it. So was born the multistage rocket, without which our modern satellites and spacecraft designed to travel to the Moon and planets of our solar system would never have been feasible.

In 1855, Colonel Boxer

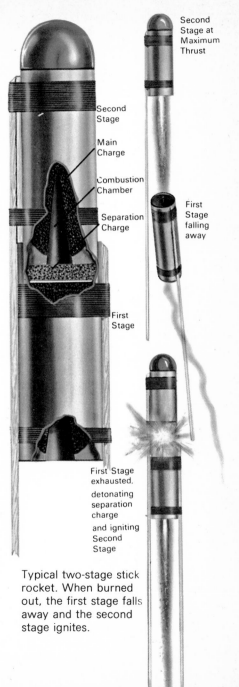

Second Stage

Main Charge

Combustion Chamber

Separation Charge

First Stage

Second Stage at Maximum Thrust

First Stage falling away

First Stage exhausted, detonating separation charge and igniting Second Stage

Typical two-stage stick rocket. When burned out, the first stage falls away and the second stage ignites.

tested the first of his famous two-stage life-line rockets, based on Frezier's ideas. These made use of two ordinary gunpowder charges, separated by a small charge of quick-burning powder, in a single tube. By the end of the nineteenth century, Boxer rockets were used at many life-saving stations. Weighing only six pounds each, they could carry a half-inch hemp line a distance of over 1,000 feet.

Similar rockets are still utilized all over the world, in conjunction with the breeches-buoy, and have saved tens of thousands of lives.

Nikolai Kibalchich designed the first rocket aircraft.

The rocket aircraft of Nikolai Kibalchich

Before the invention of the balloon, the rocket must have seemed to offer the only way of lifting anything from the surface of the Earth and carrying it over a distance, but only a handful of science fiction writers and cartoonists associated rocketry with human flight until late in the nineteenth century.

In 1881, a twenty-eight-year-old Russian named Nikolai Kibalchich attained brief fame as a member of an organization named *Narodnaya Volya* ('People's Will'), which was responsible for assassinating Czar Alexander II as he drove through the streets of St. Petersburg.

Kibalchich had helped to design the bombs used to kill the Czar. While awaiting execution shortly afterward, it seems that he conceived—a little late—a more lawful application of his knowledge of explosives. His ideas remained hidden in the police archives for thirty-seven years, until 1918, when the Revolution cast a different light on those who had plotted against the Czarist regime.

Once found, they brought new and more permanent fame to Kibalchich who, it appears, was responsible for the first known design for a rocket-powered aircraft. The precursor of modern jet-lift VTOL (vertical take-off and landing) airplanes, it consisted of a wooden platform carrying a pilot and a vertically mounted rocket combustion chamber. The idea was to feed gunpowder charges continuously into the chamber, so producing thrust to raise the craft into the air and keep it there. Kibalchich even suggested the modern technique of tilting the chamber to propel and steer the aircraft in any desired direction.

In its initial form, this pioneer design for a rocket-craft was impractical. Unfortunately, Kibalchich did not have time to develop his ideas further. If he had, he might have changed the course of history a second time.

Nine years later, a German named Hermann Ganswindt suggested the use of a similar kind of motor to power a man-carrying spaceship. Having little scientific knowledge, he did not realize that the pressure produced by burning gases was sufficient by itself to propel such a craft. He proposed that steel cartridges containing dynamite should be exploded one after the other in a combustion chamber, so that one half of the cartridge was ejected while the other half slammed against the top of the chamber to provide the reaction force. Perhaps it is as well that he did not build his spaceship!

The father of space flight

Konstantin Eduardovich Tsiolkovsky was born in humble circumstances in the town of Izhevskoye, in 1857. At the age of twenty-one he became a school-teacher at Borovsk, in the Kaluga Province of Russia, and soon made such a name for himself as a mathematician and physicist that he was not regarded as a crank when he began to study and discuss the possibilities of space flight in 1883—twenty years before anyone had even built a successful airplane.

Having decided that a reaction engine was essential to propel and steer a vehicle in space, he turned his attention to designing a rocket-powered spacecraft. The measure of his genius is shown by the fact that he specified liquid oxygen and liquid hydrogen as the propellents for his first rocket design of 1903, for these propellents are used today in the upper stages of America's Saturn V rocket, which put the first men on the Moon.

Tsiolkovsky was a theorist and did not build or test any of his designs; but he left a full record of them in scores of scientific books. His most important single contribution to space flight was, perhaps, the conclusion that only a multi-stage rocket, which he called a rocket-train, coud reach a sufficiently high speed to overcome the 'pull' of Earth's gravity and escape into space.

He had no doubt of the immense thrust that would be required, and his best known design, for 'a passenger rocket-train of the year 2017', was made up of no fewer than twenty stages with a total length of more than 300 feet. Tsiolkovsky explained that as each stage in succession used up all its propellents it would fall away, so reducing the weight of structure that had to be accelerated to still higher speed by the remaining stages. He knew that vast quantities of pro-pellents would be needed and calculated that they would weigh at least four times as much as the entire rocket structure and payload.

He also realized that rockets would need to withstand the high temperatures built up by air friction as they passed through the atmosphere. Thus, the passenger cabin of his rocket-train was triple-skinned, with the outer skin made of a highly refractory metal.

Tsiolkovsky (portrait on page 144) died in 1935, long before his dreams began to come true, but he will be remembered always as the first man to point the way to the stars.

One of Tsiolkovsky's designs for a three-stage rocket-train. By continuous transfer of fuel from the boosters, the final stage still has full tanks when all boosters have burned out and fallen away.

Goddard used 'The Hearse' to tow his rockets to the launch tower.

From Jules Verne to Robert Goddard

Although books such as Jules Verne's *From the Earth to the Moon,* written more than a century ago, were simply pioneer works of science fiction, few people realize what an important part they played in the history of the rocket. Tsiolkovsky's interest in space travel was inspired by the writings of Jules Verne; the same is true of two other great pioneers of rocketry— Hermann Oberth and Robert Goddard.

Born in Hungary in 1894, Oberth later became a German citizen. During World War I he put before the German War Department his ideas for a long-range liquid-propellent bombardment rocket. When rebuffed, he transferred his interest to rockets for space flight and in 1923 published a small book entitled *The Rocket into Interplanetary Space.* In this he explained how a rocket could travel in the vacuum of space or be used to put a satellite into orbit around the Earth. He even went into such details as the effects of space flight on the human body.

Oberth designed some relatively advanced rockets and tested one or two of them, without much success. He is remembered therefore, like Tsiolkovsky, mainly as one who inspired the men who later translated fiction and theory into hot gas and metal.

Robert Goddard, an American physics professor, began by designing rockets for the armed forces. His research soon

16

showed the limitations of solid (powder) propellents. Assisted by grants from the Smithsonian Institution, he built a tiny liquid-propellent engine that ran successfully on a test-bench in 1923. After three more years he was ready to attempt the first launching of a liquid-propellent rocket—a spidery device, ten feet long, consisting of a liquid oxygen tank and smaller gasoline tank linked by slim pipelines to a combustion chamber at the top.

On March 16, 1926, this rocket covered a distance of 184 feet at a speed of 64 mph, at Auburn, Massachusetts. Further tests followed, and in 1929 Charles Lindbergh, the famous transatlantic pilot, persuaded the wealthy Daniel Guggenheim to provide $50,000, an amount sufficient enough for Goddard to devote his full time to rocket experiments. By 1935 he had progressed to an 84-pound rocket, 15 feet long, which climbed one and a half miles at a speed of 700 mph.

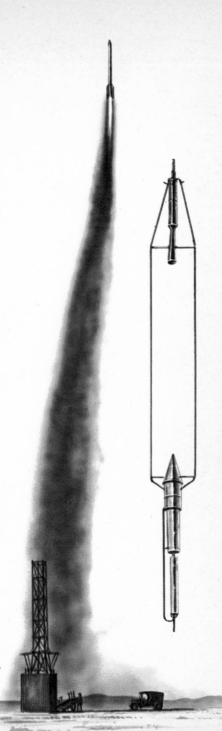

Goddard's 1926 rocket (*right*) and the launch of his gyroscopically stabilized type (1937).

Germany sets the pace

Goddard continued his experiments, with growing success, until he died in 1945, but the United States government was slow to recognize the value of his work. Meanwhile, Russia established several official organizations to follow up the pioneering work of Tsiolkovsky. Headed by Fridrikh Tsander and Valentin Glushko, Soviet design teams had liquid oxygen and gasoline powered rocket engines under test by 1930, and by 1936 were achieving considerable success with rockets like the 213-pound Aviavnito, which reached a height of three and a half miles.

Batteries of Sander solid-propellent rockets enabled car manufacturer Fritz von Opel to fly at 95 mph in this glider and to reach 125 mph in the Rak 2 racing car in 1928. The top picture is of the tail-first Ente sailplane which was the first rocket plane to fly successfully.

However, it was Germany that became the acknowledged leader in rocketry in the 1930's and early 1940's. This was not surprising, for the restrictions on flying imposed by the Versailles Peace Treaty were so frustrating to adventurous young Germans that they could not fail to be attracted by the possibilities of the rocket.

Some of the earliest experiments were more spectacular than significant. Fritz von Opel, the famous car manufacturer, paid for the conversion of a racing car into the Opel-Rak 1, powered by a battery of Sander solid-propellent rockets of the kind used for life-line rescue at sea. In the best of a series of tests, in 1928, this vehicle reached 70 mph. It was followed by the Opel-Rak 2 in which Opel himself clocked 125 mph on May 23, 1928, propelled by twenty-four rockets.

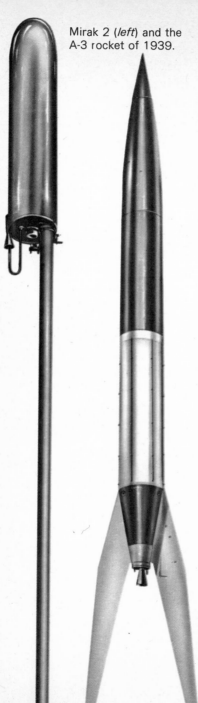

Mirak 2 (*left*) and the A-3 rocket of 1939.

Before long, rockets were being used to power experimental rail-cars, sledges and even gliders. The first rocket-plane to fly successfully was the tail-first Ente sailplane. Two Sander rockets enabled it to cover three-quarters of a mile in just over one minute on June 11, 1928. Three months later, Fritz von Opel flew at 95 mph in a more conventional glider powered by 16 Sander rockets, each developing 50 pounds of thrust.

In retrospect, von Opel's experiments are seen mainly as publicity stunts, but far more serious experiments were soon taking place in Reinickendorf, a suburb of Berlin. In 1930, on an abandoned ammunition dump which they called their *Raketenflugplatz* (rocket airfield), a group of young enthusiasts belonging to the Verein für Raumschiffahrt (VfR, Society for Space Travel) began testing rockets that were destined to change the whole pattern of future warfare.

VfR to V-2

When a young student named Wernher von Braun joined the newly formed VfR in 1927, he and his fellow-members thought of the rocket mainly as a vehicle

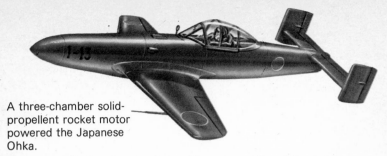

A three-chamber solid-
propellent rocket motor
powered the Japanese
Ohka.

for space flight. Inspired by Hermann Oberth's writings, they first built a small rocket which they named Mirak 1, signifying 'Minimum Raket'. Powered by liquid oxygen and gasoline, it was ingenious in that its body—which was only about twelve inches long—formed the liquid oxygen tank and shrouded the combustion chamber in such a way that the oxygen cooled the chamber. The gasoline was carried in a three-foot-long tubular 'tail-stick'.

Mirak 1 was destroyed when its oxygen tank burst in September 1930. The same fate befell Mirak 2 in the spring of 1931. Undeterred, the VfR produced a completely new type of rocket called the Repulsor 1, in which the motor was cooled by water stored inside the double-skin walls. This rocket was launched to a height of 200 feet on May 14, 1931. By August, improved Repulsor 4 rockets were being sent to a height of a mile and then recovered by parachute.

Within three years, financial problems and the antagonism of Hitler's new Nazi regime to any organization with international ties led to the end of private rocket experiments in Germany, and von Braun found himself working for the German army at the nearby military testing ground at Kummersdorf.

Germany's Me 163 tailless fighter reached 596 mph on the power of a 3,750-lb. thrust liquid-propellent rocket motor.

Events moved quickly and dramatically. Under the leadership of Captain (later Major-General) Walter Dornberger and von Braun, the army built and tested two A-2 liquid-propellent rockets, which reached 6,500 feet. In 1937, all work was transferred to a secret new base at Peenemünde on the Baltic coast. By 1939, the 21-foot A-3 rocket, burning liquid oxygen and alcohol, had reached the record height of seven and a half miles. What few people knew was that it was a smaller version of a bombardment rocket known as A-4.

The A-4 itself was tested with complete success on October 3, 1942, reaching a height of 50 miles and covering a range of 120 miles. On September 8, 1944, an A-4, now redesignated V-2 (*Vergeltungswaffen*—reprisal weapons) dropped on London at 3,500 mph, five minutes after taking off from near The Hague. The day of the push-button weapon had dawned.

Rockets in World War II

The German V-2 (A-4), illustrated on page 25, was the most advanced rocket used in World War II. Over forty-six feet long, it weighed more than twelve tons and carried a one-ton warhead. About 1,115 rockets fell on Southern England in seven months, killing 2,855 people. V-2 was a new and terrifying kind of weapon, against which there was no defense save the destruction or capture of the launching sites.

The V-2 offensive came too late and on too small a scale to influence the outcome of the war; but, together with the American atomic bomb, it demonstrated that any future war—in which far better rockets would carry far more power-

Katyusha battery in action on the Russian front.

V-1 flying bomb.

Rocket-firing Typhoons attacking German armored vehicles.

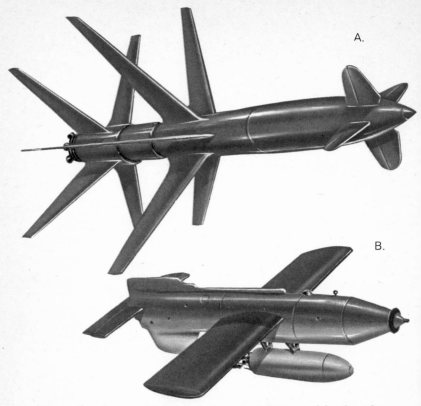

A.

B.

ful warheads—could lead to the annihilation of both sides.

Its partner in Hitler's *Vergeltungswaffen* offensive was V-1, a small pilotless aircraft powered by a pulsejet engine, the raucous noise of which earned it the name 'buzz-bomb' from its intended victims. A total of 7,547 V-1s were launched against Britain, each carrying 1,870 pounds of explosives. They had no real guidance system, simply flying a pre-set course until a time-switch cut off the fuel supply and caused them to dive on whatever lay below. Their speed of 390 mph put them at the mercy of the defenses, and 1,847 were destroyed by fighter aircraft, 1,866 by anti-aircraft guns, 232 by flying into barrage balloon cables and 12 by the Royal Navy. Those that got through killed 6,139 people.

Much simpler than these pioneer strategic missiles were the

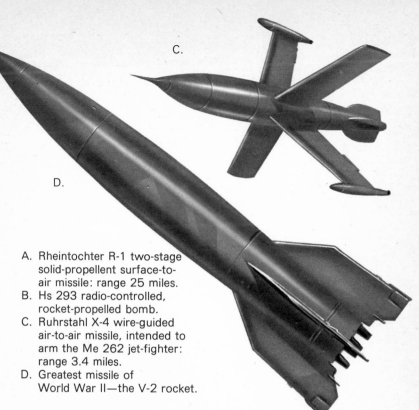

C.

D.

A. Rheintochter R-1 two-stage
   solid-propellent surface-to-
   air missile: range 25 miles.
B. Hs 293 radio-controlled,
   rocket-propelled bomb.
C. Ruhrstahl X-4 wire-guided
   air-to-air missile, intended to
   arm the Me 262 jet-fighter:
   range 3.4 miles.
D. Greatest missile of
   World War II—the V-2 rocket.

solid-propellent unguided rockets fired from surface vehicles and aircraft. Best-known of the surface-to-surface rockets was Russia's Katyusha, launched from multi-tube batteries mounted on trucks. Six feet long, it weighed 92½ pounds and had a range of three miles.

The most successful rocket-fighter was the RAF's Typhoon. Carrying four 60-pound rockets under each wing it pioneered the 'cab-rank' technique, in which a controller on the ground called in a squadron of Typhoons by radio and directed them against a target which the aircraft then attacked in line astern. Whole German divisions were massacred in such attacks following the Allied invasion of France in June 1944.

Hitler's secret weapons
No other nation has produced such a variety of advanced weapons in so brief a period as did Germany in World War II.

Outnumbered and outclassed in conventional warfare, she tried to avert defeat by evolving entirely new kinds of weapons for both attack and defense.

In addition to V-1 and V-2, the Germans used operationally a four-stage solid-propellent bombardment rocket called the Rheinbote. It weighed 3,773 pounds at launch, but carried less than fifty pounds of explosive. In January 1945, sixty Rheinbotes were fired against Antwerp, with little effect.

The only other missiles used in action were the radio-controlled Ruhrstahl SD 1400X free-falling armor-piercing bomb and Henschel Hs 293 rocket-propelled high-explosive bomb. About a hundred SD 1400Xs were dropped from

The rocket-powered Ba 349 Natter interceptor was intended to be launched vertically from a ramp for a one-pass attack on Allied bombers with its nose-mounted rocket armament. In the one and only attempt at a piloted launch, the pilot was killed.

Based on the Me 163 fighter, Enzian was a 13ft-span ramp-launched surface-to-air missile with a range of 16 miles. Construction was mainly of wood.

Dornier Do 217 bombers, their greatest success being the sinking of the 42,000-ton Italian battleship *Roma*, which broke in two following direct hits after the Italian surrender in September 1943. One month earlier, H.M.S. *Egret* had been sunk by an Hs 293 in the Bay of Biscay. A total of 1,700 Hs 293s were built and continued in use until the end of the war, their efficiency lessened by inadequate training of the launch crews and Allied jamming of their radio control system.

The illustrations on these and the two preceding pages show not only operational weapons but others which were designed in a desperate attempt to offset numerical inferiority and muddled leadership.

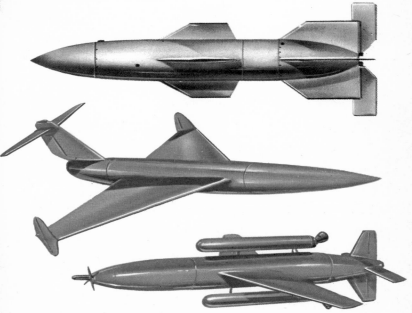

Based on V-2, but smaller, Wasserfall was a liquid-propellent surface-to-air missile with a designed range of sixteen miles. It was radio-controlled. No German surface-to-air missile became operational.

Feuerlilie was an experimental rocket-powered surface-to-air missile of 1943–44 vintage.

The Schmetterling liquid-propellent surface-to-air missile was ordered into production in 1944 but was too late to be used in action.

CONTROL AND GUIDANCE OF MISSILES

The inside story

The simplest military rocket consists of a tube of solid propellent with fixed tail-fins at the rear and a high-explosive warhead. The only complication is that the propellent is usually molded with an elaborate cross section, to ensure that the greatest possible area of propellent is burned at one time. This enables it to produce a large volume of gas far more rapidly than simply burning a single stick of propellent of the same weight from one end to the other, like a cigarette.

Having produced a large volume of gas, the next important factor is to get rid of it as quickly as possible That is why all rockets—even the firework type—eject their exhaust gases through a hole much smaller than the diameter of the casing. Known as a venturi, this narrowing-down of the nozzle has the effect of increasing the speed of the escaping gases; as a rough guide, doubling the exhaust velocity doubles the speed of the rocket.

For this reason, most large

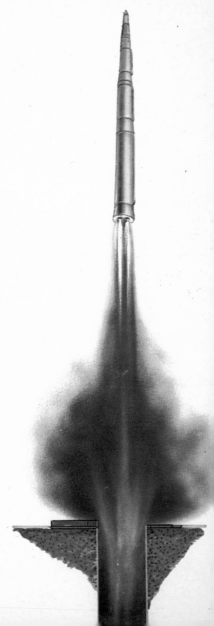

Minuteman (*right*), cut away to show the rocket chambers of the three stages, and the guidance 'black boxes' beneath the warhead. (*Below*) leaving its launch silo.

Warhead

Inertial Guidance

Instrumentation
Bay

4 Vectorable
Nozzles

4 Vec. Noz

4 Vec. Noz

space rockets have liquid-propellent engines, because liquid propellants produce far more energy in the form of fast-moving exhaust gases than do the old-fashioned gunpowder type of solid propellents. Unfortunately, they add to the rocket's complexity, as tanks are needed to contain them, and pumps and valves to control their flow in very precise quantities to the combustion chamber.

Further complication comes when we try to improve the accuracy of the rocket by adding a guidance and control system.

Perfection of the first big American liquid-propellent inter-continental ballistic missiles (ICBM), Atlas and Titan, probably represented the most difficult single engineering project undertaken by man up to that time. The subsequent switch to solid propellents has made their replacement, the Minuteman, smaller and simpler. But the original nuclear warhead has had to give way to a multiple type, containing decoys and other countermeasures to confuse defending anti-missile missiles. So an ICBM remains a complex, costly weapon.

Honest John artillery rockets on their mobile launchers. They are so destructive, they need no guidance system.

(*Left*) Littejohn rocket being transported under an S-58 helicopter.

(*Below*) Russian FROG-1 artillery rocket on its tracked transporter/launcher. Able to carry a nuclear warhead some 15 miles, this rocket has been in service since 1957.

The new artillery

Many armies continue to use simple tube-launched rockets on the lines of the American infantry's Bazooka anti-tank rocket and Russia's wartime Katyusha. In addition, larger types of rockets have been produced to replace or supplement artillery in attacks on heavily fortified positions.

One of the first was America's Honest John, powered by a solid-propellent motor and carried on a standard truck. Since its nuclear warhead creates such a huge area of devastation, it needs no guidance system, even over a range of twelve miles. Instead, Honest John is spun immediately after launch by a number of small rockets, exhausting behind its bulbous warhead. The spin-stabilization is then maintained by its canted tail-fins.

Only six men are needed to fire Honest John. Littlejohn is even smaller, with a length of 14 feet 5 inches and weight of only 780 pounds, yet it, too, can carry a nuclear warhead more than ten miles. Its launcher can be towed by a jeep and is small enough to be hauled by a helicopter to firing sites in rugged terrain.

Russia's counterparts are the FROG (Free Rocket Over Ground) family, carried on amphibious tracked transporter/launchers. Seven different FROGs have been identified, with ranges of fifteen to thirty miles and with alternative nuclear or high-explosive warheads. All have single- or two-stage solid-propellent moters and are spin-stabilized.

This drawing shows a Mace-A 'flying bomb' of the USAF on its Translauncher transport/ launch trailer, hauled by a Tera-cruzer tractor. The huge tires of both vehicles can be inflated or deflated automatically to suit varying terrain. Mace's wings are folded while it is in transit.

The smaller drawings show an earlier Matador missile (*right*) and Mace-B, which is usually housed in an underground hangar at instant readiness.

Improved flying bombs

Impressed by German wartime missile development, the United States Armed Forces began their own programs of missile design in 1944. The U.S. Army Air Force concentrated first on subsonic 'flying bombs' rather than supersonic ballistic missiles of the V-2 type—an approach which reflected its experience in operating winged aircraft and took into account the relative inaccuracy of V-2 which could seldom be expected to land within three to five miles of its target.

The Air Force's earliest operational bombardment missiles were the Matador, with a range of 650 miles, which entered service in 1955, and the huge Snark, which could carry a 5,000-pound nuclear warhead more than six thousand miles at just below the speed of sound. Both were powered by jet-engines and were fairly vulnerable to interception, although Snark was able to make its attack at low altitude and had an unjammable

inertial/star-tracking guidance system.

Matador used a simple radio-navigation guidance system, in which a receiver on board the missile picked up radio signals transmitted from two ground stations and used them to work out its position automatically. It was replaced eventually by the improved Mace, with two alternative unjammable guidance systems. The version fitted in the TM-76A Mace-A compared data on a film strip with the terrain beneath the missile in flight and corrected any deviation from course. The inertial guidance system of the TM-76B Mace-B used accelerometers and gyroscopes to measure every slight change of direction of the missile in flight and then passed signals to the control system to put the missile back on course. Inertial guidance systems are fitted to a high proportion of modern long-range missiles.

'Styx' leaving a Komar-class patrol boat.

The sinking of the 'Eilat'

On October 21, 1967, the Egyptian Navy located the Israeli destroyer *Eilat* about twelve miles off-shore from Port Said. Smarting from the defeat inflicted on their armed services by Israel a few months earlier, they decided to demonstrate dramatically that they still retained some powerful weapons and the readiness to use them.

On board Osa-class fast patrol boats supplied by Russia, naval personnel prepared to launch the rocket-powered flying-bomb missiles which form the primary armament of such vessels. Nobody had ever before used weapons of this kind to attack a ship at sea, but the chance of success was increased by the fact that the crew of the *Eilat*, not being officially at war, would not expect to be attacked. Also, the target was so close that there was no need for the Osas to leave harbor and launch their missiles in the rougher open sea.

When the missiles raced down on the *Eilat*, the destroyer's crew were taken completely by surprise, and direct hits sank their ship in a matter of minutes.

The type of missile used by the Egyptians was neither new nor secret. Known in the West by the code-name 'Styx', it is a small pilotless airplane with a wing spand of about 8 feet 10 inches and a length of 20 feet. Each Osa-class patrol boat carries four, on launch-rails inside small containers on the rear deck; the smaller Komar-class boats carry two.

Like the American Mace, 'Styx' is launched with the aid of a solid-propellent rocket, attached under its rear fuselage and jettisoned when it is burned out. Its main rocket engine appears to give it a high subsonic speed. Most surprising aspect of the *Eilat* action was the accuracy of 'Styx' over what was approaching its maximum range. This suggests that it has an efficient radar homing system.

At one time, the United States Navy had a somewhat similar weapon, the jet-powered Regulus, which was launched from submarines and carried a nuclear warhead. Regulus was superseded by the Polaris ballistic rocket. Russia, on the other hand, continues to have great faith in the flying bomb and has some in service that are much bigger, newer and more formidable than 'Styx'.

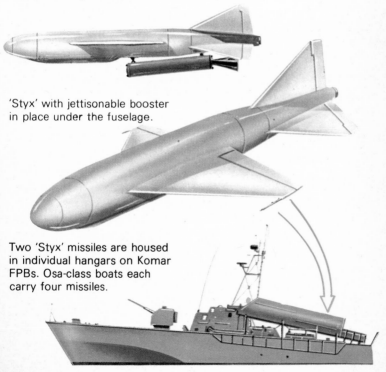

'Styx' with jettisonable booster in place under the fuselage.

Two 'Styx' missiles are housed in individual hangars on Komar FPBs. Osa-class boats each carry four missiles.

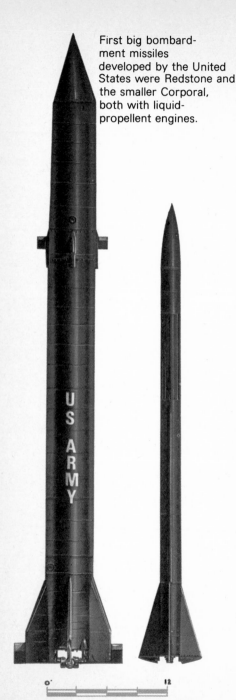

First big bombard-
ment missiles
developed by the United
States were Redstone and
the smaller Corporal,
both with liquid-
propellent engines.

Learning from V-2

Both the United States and
Russia gained their first experience of launching big
rockets with captured V-2s.
They then set to work to
develop improved versions of
the V-2, with the help of the
original designers.

Wernher von Braun was
put in charge of a team of engineers at the U.S. Army's Redstone Arsenal in Alabama,
and their first project was
named after the Arsenal. Its
engine, built by the Rocketdyne Company, was based on
that of V-2 and used the same
liquid oxygen and alcohol
propellents. One major improvement was that the entire
propulsion system was jettisoned after burnout, leaving the guidance and warhead
package to continue alone on
a ballistic trajectory to the
target. Other advances were
the provision of interchangeable nuclear or high-explosive
warheads and the installation
of inertial guidance to improve accuracy.

Redstone became opera-
tional in 1956, and even after
it had been replaced by more
advanced missiles was put to
good use as the booster for
the first flights by America's
Mercury astronauts (see
pages 96–7).

0   12

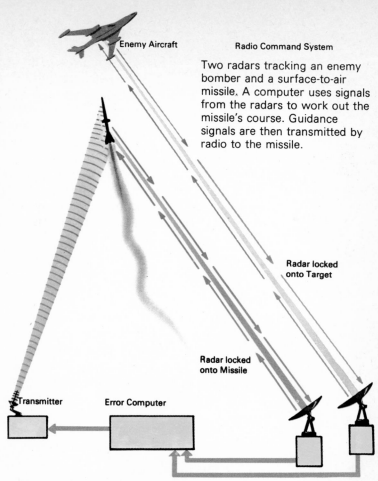

Enemy Aircraft

Radio Command System

Two radars tracking an enemy bomber and a surface-to-air missile. A computer uses signals from the radars to work out the missile's course. Guidance signals are then transmitted by radio to the missile.

Radar locked onto Target

Radar locked onto Missile

Transmitter

Error Computer

In parallel service with it for many years was the smaller Corporal rocket, powered by an engine which ran on nitric acid and aniline propellents and gave it a range of seventy-five miles. With Corporal, the required trajectory and engine burning time were entered as dial settings on the missile before launch; but small corrections could be made by radio command during flight. This involved tracking the missile's position by radar, calculating if it was on course, and passing signals by radio to its guidance and control system by a similar technique to that used to steer radio-controlled model airplanes—and the anti-aircraft missile shown above.

Russia's first big rockets

For ten years after the war everyone in the West wondered how much progress Russia was making in the design and production of military rockets. Soviet secrecy gave birth to endless rumors. It was suggested that behind the Iron Curtain captured German scientists from Peenemünde had continued work on projects like the A-9. This was similar to the V-2, but had wings so that, instead of hurtling to the ground after burn-out, it would be able to glide up to four hundred miles, so extending the range of the missile.

Some of the speculation ended in 1957, when five different types of missile were included in a parade through Moscow celebrating the fortieth anniversary of the October Revolution. The largest of these weapons, which later received the NATO code-name 'Shyster', was estimated to be sixty feet long and to have a range of about seven hundred miles. It was clearly a liquid-propellent rocket, based on V-2 technology, and was assumed to carry alternative nuclear or high-explosive warheads.

'Shyster' was, in fact, the world's first IRBM (intermediate-range ballistic missile), having made its first flight in April 1956. This preceded by about one year its U.S. counterparts, the Jupiter and Thor; however, these were more advanced missiles, similar in size but with a range of 1,725 miles.

There were several reasons for the better performance of the American IRBMs. Their Rocketdyne engines, running on liquid oxygen and kerosene and giving about 150,000 pounds of thrust, were a big step forward from the V-2 engine. In addition, America had made greater progress than Russia in reducing the bulk of her nuclear warheads. This gave the United States the option of building smaller rockets to do the same job—as it did in the case of its ICBMs (inter-continental bal-

The 'Shyster' IRBM.

FROG-3, one of the standard Soviet unguided battlefield rockets with a range of about thirty miles.

listic missiles)—or of obtaining longer range from rockets of similar size—as it did with its IRBMs.

With its propellent tanks lengthened by 8 feet, 'Shyster' became the 1,100-mile range 'Sandal', the missile that caused a crisis in 1962 when Russia tried to deploy it in Cuba until forced to withdraw by United States diplomatic pressure. Nor was this the limit of development of what is now a very old design, for Russia's latest 'Skean' IRBM is basically a longer (75 feet) and fatter (8 feet diameter) version of 'Sandal', with a range of up to two thousand miles. All of the family are believed to utilize an inertial guidance system.

New life for bombers

In 1944–45 Germany tried to improve the effectiveness of its
V-1 flying bombs by launching them in mid-air from Heinkel
He 111 bombers. This eliminated the need for ground launch-
sites, which were vulnerable to Allied air attack, and extended
the range of the V-1s, which could be launched over the sea or
over Britain itself. It also meant that they could be directed toward their target from almost any direction, instead of only
from known areas of the continent, and this complicated the
task of Britain's air defenses.

Another advantage of launching self-propelled missiles from
an airplane is that the launch-plane can make its attack without
itself approaching close to the target. This has become of
increasing importance since the war. Without the benefit of
the air-launched missile, large bombers would now be relatively easy prey for a defense system equipped with modern
early-warning radar, anti-aircraft missiles and radar-guided
fighters armed with homing missiles.

(*Opposite page, top*) the anti-shipping version of Russia's Tu-16 bomber carries a jet-propelled 'Kennel' missile under each wing. A far more formidable combination is the USAF's mighty B-52 Stratofortress (*opposite, bottom*) armed with two Hound Dogs, fitted with H-bomb warheads.

The RAF's Vulcan Mk 2, which can carry Blue Steel H-bomb missiles.

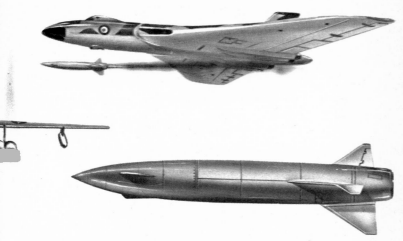

As a result the bomber's life has been extended into the 1970's, even if it may need to make its attack at low altitude, in an effort to slip beneath the searching eyes of enemy radar. It also needs to carry a wide variety of countermeasures devices, ranging from the metal-foil 'window', dropped in World War II in order to clutter enemy radar screens, to decoy flares which attract infra-red (head-seeking) air-to-air and surface-to-air missiles fired against them, and the carcinotron which jams all radio and radar trasmissions over a wide area.

Air-to-surface missiles carried by bombers are often called stand-off bombs as they enable the launch-plane to 'stand off' the target at a safe distance. Typical of the largest and most formidable types now in service are those shown here.

The Hound Dog carried by America's B-52 Stratofortress is jet-powered and can find its own way to a target more than six hundred miles from where it is launched, cruising at 1,300 mph. Also jet-powered, but much less advanced, is the 'Kennel' missile carried by Russia's Tu-16 bomber.

41

Britain's Blue Steel, carried by the Vulcan, has a range of only some two hundred miles but its rocket-engine enables it to fly at several times the speed of sound at very great heights, making it more difficult to intercept. Like Hound Dog, it has an inertial guidance system and thermonuclear warhead.

Weapons for ground attack

Deadly though they were, the types of rocket fired against ground targets from aircraft like the Typhoon, in World War II, were primitive by comparison with the ground attack weapons of today. The addition of a guidance system and the use of powerful new propellents has given even small air-to-surface missiles such range and accuracy that the pilot of the launch aircraft need no longer 'fly down the gun barrels' of the target he is attacking.

The French AS 12 air-to-surface missile is normally steered into the target by movement of a tiny joystick in the cockpit of the launch aircraft. This transmits guidance signals to the missile over two fine wires which unwind as the AS 12 travels through the air Alternatively, as illustrated here, the AS 12 can utilize TCA automatic guidance, described on page 47.

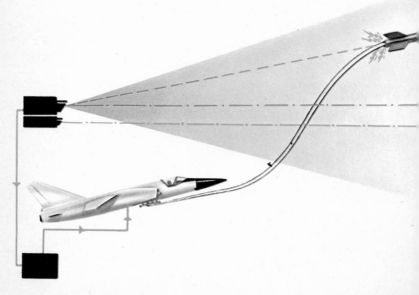

Most widely used of the current air-to-surface missiles is the American Bullpup, which is steered to the target by the pilot of the launch aircraft, using a small joystick on a radio control box in the cockpit. This is known as radio command guidance.

The original Bullpup had a solid-propellent motor and was built around a standard 250-pound bomb. Current versions have liquid-propellent motors and improved warheads, some of them nuclear.

Walleye is unpowered and is guided to the target by a television camera in its nose. Once the pilot has focused this camera on the target, the missile homes on it automatically. A similar system is used in one version of the Anglo-French Martel; the other (anti-radar) version homes automatically on the emissions from enemy radar, as does the American Shrike.

The American Bullpup B missile has a liquid-propellent motor and radio command guidance. Range is ten miles.

The glass 'eye' at the nose of each of the two lower missiles covers a tiny television camera by which they are guided into their targets. The missiles are Walleye (*above*) and Martel.

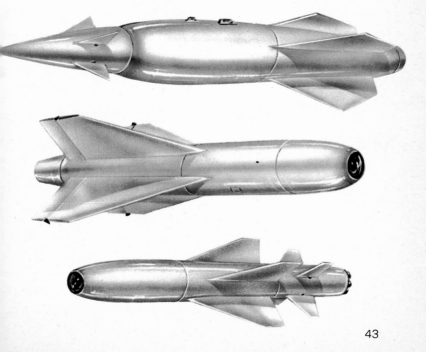

Quail is a unique decoy missile. Launched in mid-air from a B-52 bomber, it confuses the enemy radar plotters by producing the same blip on their screens as does the huge B-52.

The wire-guided AS 11 air-to-surface missile is carried by both fixed-wing aircraft and helicopters.

Confuse and destroy

Some of the most important weapons carried by modern fighters and bombers are intended solely to help the aircraft to get through to their target without being shot down en route. Shrike and the anti-radar version of Martel, described on the previous page, are weapons of this kind. By destroying the enemy's radar installations, they would prevent him from locating the attacking aircraft and directing their interception by missiles or fighters.

An earlier bomber defense missile, intended to confuse rather than to destroy enemy radar, is the American jet-powered Quail. Less than thirteen feet long, it can be folded in such a way that it takes up only a small space in the bomb-bay of a B-52 bomber. When released, its wings flip open and it starts tearing around the sky on a carefully planned course of several hundred miles. As it does so, electronic equipment packed inside its reinforced-plastic body transmits signals which jam the enemy radar or give an image on the radar screens as large as that of the B-52. This prevents the enemy from sorting out the bomber from the decoy.

A very different kind of missile is the French Nord AS 11. Only 47 inches long, with a weight of 66 pounds, it can be fired from subsonic aircraft against surface targets such as tanks and submarines and will penetrate 24 inches of steel armor. Guidance is by radio command, by means of a small control stick, the signals being passed to the missile through two fine wires which unwind as it travels through the air, keeping it linked to the aircraft until the warhead explodes. The AS 11 has a range of nearly two miles.

Tiny tank-killers

The AS 11 missile illustrated on page 44 is an air-to-surface adaptation of Nord's SS 11 anti-tank missile, which is used by the armies of eighteen different countries. By mounting a

Small enough to be operated by a single infantryman, the Vigilant wire-guided anti-tank missile will penetrate twenty-two inches of armor.

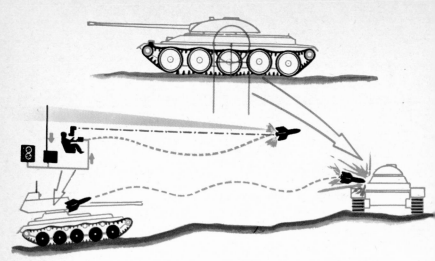

Diagram showing an attack on an enemy tank with an SS 11 missile, using radio command gudiance.

Three standard anti-tank wire-guided missiles are the SS 12 (*above*). Vigilant (*below*) and Swingfire (*bottom*).

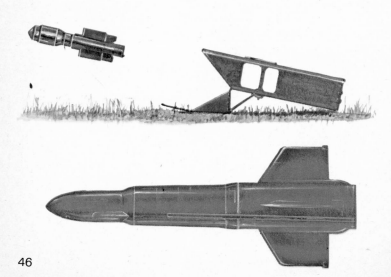

launcher for four SS 11s on the gun turret of their tanks, the French ensure a 360° field of fire for the missiles, which are wire-guided and spin-stabilized and travel to the target at 360 mph.

Even these small weapons are very lethal. As an alternative to an anti-tank warhead capable of piercing twenty-four inches of armor plate, they can be fitted with a high-fragmentation anti-personnel type, or another which will penetrate an armored steel plate half an inch thick at a range of nearly two miles and explode about seven feet behind the point of impact.

The SS 12 is similar, but larger, with a warhead as heavy as the complete SS 11 missile. This makes it effective against fortifications as well as tanks, ships and vehicles. Like the SS 11, it can be carried by aircraft and ships and can utilize Nord's new TCA (*Télécommande Automatique*) guidance system.

When using TCA guidance, all the operator has to do is keep the target centered in an optical sight. The missile is 'captured' after launch by an infra-red device which picks up the heat from flares mounted on the rear of the missile. It measures the angle of the missile's flight path relative to the operator's line of sight and passes the information to a computer. After working out the signals that must be passed to the missile's control system to steer it on course for the target, the computer transmits the signals. The whole procedure is so quick that a TCA-guided SS 12 can be used against moving targets only four hundred yards from the launching point.

Other illustrations show two standard wire-guided anti-tank missiles used by the British Army. Vigilant is small enough to be operated by a single infantry soldier, yet will penetrate twenty-two inches of armor plate at a range of one mile. It is so controllable that, after a few hours on a training simulator, soldiers often hit the target the first time they fire one of the missiles.

Swingfire is a newer and more powerful weapon, which can be steered through a considerable angle in any direction after it leaves its launcher. It remains sealed in its container until fired, when it breaks through the foil that covers one end of the container to keep out dirt during storage and transport.

Soviet anti-tank missiles

The anti-tank missiles in service with the armies of Russia and its allies are comparable in size and efficiency to those built in the West and use similar wire-guidance systems. What makes them of particular interest is the ingenious way in which they are carried on their launch vehicles.

The earliest Soviet missile in this category was given the code-name 'Snapper' by NATO. Examples captured from the Egyptians by the Israeli army in June 1967 were mounted on a quadruple launcher on a GAZ-69 (Jeep-type) light cross-country vehicle. The launcher was pivoted in such a way that the missiles were transported vertically and then swung down by means of a hand crank to fire rearward over the back of the

Latest Soviet anti-tank missile is 'Sagger'. Six wire-guided missiles of this type are carried by the BRDM amphibious vehicle (*below*) on a retractable launcher which remains under an armored cover when extended for firing. On the opposite page is another BRDM carrying four 'Swatters', plus a detail drawing of 'Swatter'.

vehicle. Another crank enabled the operator to traverse the launcher.

In the Soviet army 'Snapper', the larger 'Swatter' and the new and smaller 'Sagger' are all now carried on the BRDM armored amphibious vehicle. This has a propeller in a water duct at the rear, for propulsion on water, and four small retractable wheels under its center-body, which can be lowered to improve its performance over rough country.

Six 'Saggers' can be carried on a BRDM, an interesting feature being that when the launcher is extended for firing it remains protected by the armored cover plate that encloses it within the vehicle during transport.

Have missile, will travel

The big snag with the first generation of field artillery missiles produced after the war was that they were cumbersome and could not be fired quickly. Their propellents had to be put aboard immediately before launching and consisted of liquids such as nitric acid and liquid oxygen which were difficult and potentially dangerous to handle. As a result, a U.S. Army battalion equipped with Corporals could fire no more than four missiles during the first day of a war, followed by one missile every twelve hours afterward.

Slow rate of fire was only one of the problems. The liquid propellents had to be transported in special tanker vehicles, and the launch crew had to wear protective suits (something like a fireman's asbestos suit) when loading the propellents into the rocket.

Today all that has been changed. The switch to either solid propellents, or new storable liquid propellents that can be kept for long periods sealed inside the missiles, means that a rocket can be fired very quickly after reaching its launch site. Care has also been taken to ensure that modern solid-propellent missiles like Sergeant and Pershing, which replaced Corporal and Redstone respectively, can be carried with their ground equipment in standard transport aircraft of the U.S. Air Force.

Most modern missiles are air-transportable, with all their ground support equipment.
A. The Sergeant guided field artillery rocket goes easily into the C-141A StarLifter transport, shown here to a smaller scale.
B. The huge cargo hold of the An-22 will accommodate several missiles like 'Scud' on their transporter/launchers.
C. Designed to replace Honest John, the U.S. Army's Lance is shown here with a C-133 Cargomaster. All the transport aircraft illustrated have rear loading doors; the C-5A also has an upward-hinged nose door.

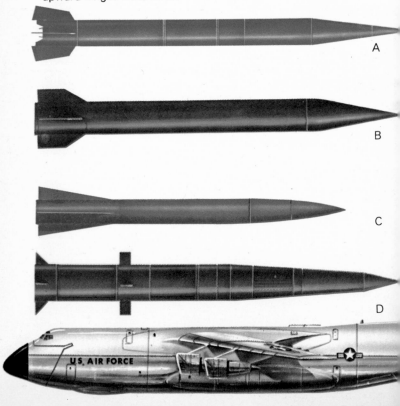

A

B

C

D

U.S. AIR FORCE

Air mobility on this scale requires transport aircraft not only large enough to take the biggest missiles in service but with wide loading doors, ramps, winches and strengthened freight floors for rapid loading and unloading of the rockets and their vehicles.

The illustrations on these two pages show military transport aircraft in service in the United States, Russia and Western Europe, and some of the missiles they are able to carry.

D. The Pershing, which has a range of up to 460 miles, can be airlifted on its erector-launch vehicle by transports ranging from the C-130 Hercules to the C-5A Galaxy (illustrated). Largest airplane yet flown, it is drawn to the same scale as the Lightning fighter and Transall freighter below.

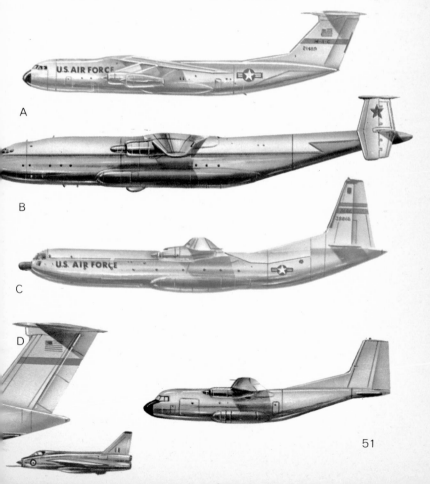

A

B

C

D

More than a missile

To the uninitiated, a guided missile is simply a rocket carrying a guidance and control system and a warhead. In fact, the rocket itself can be compared with a shell fired from a gun, in that it is useless without some form of launcher, a vehicle to transport it and other ground equipment to service it and, usually, to ensure that it follows a correct path to the target. The whole conglomeration makes up what is known as a weapon system.

In the early days some weapon systems were tremendously complex. It was stated, for example, that the ground equipment for the American Nike-Ajax surface-to-air missile contained one and a half million individual parts. Great efforts have been made by designers to reduce the volume of ground equipment needed by their missiles, in order to make them more mobile, more reliable and easier to prepare and launch. The switch to solid propellents and storable liquid propellents helped, as it eliminated the need for special tankers and fuelers to carry the difficult-to-handle liquids.

America's Pershing 1A is a typical modern artillery missile, with a range of from 115 to 460 miles. The complete weapon system is mounted on four standard 5-ton truck chassis, each of which can be carried by the USAF's comparatively small C-130 Hercules transport aircraft.

First of the vehicles is the erector-launcher, an articulated truck and trailer combination, carrying the detached nuclear warhead and the missile itself and capable of traveling on both paved roads and cross-country. The programmer-test station and power station vehicle test the missile before launch and feed into it the data which ensure that it will follow the correct path to the target. The other two vehicles are the firing battery operations center truck and the radio terminal set vehicle which carries an inflatable disc-shape radio antenna on its roof.

The smaller the missile, the less ground support equipment it needs as a rule. The Russians are particularly ingenious in the design of integrated transporter-erector-launch vehicles for weapons like their 'Scud' guided artillery missile; but even the 'Scud' weapon system needs other support vehicles, possibly for power supply and communications.

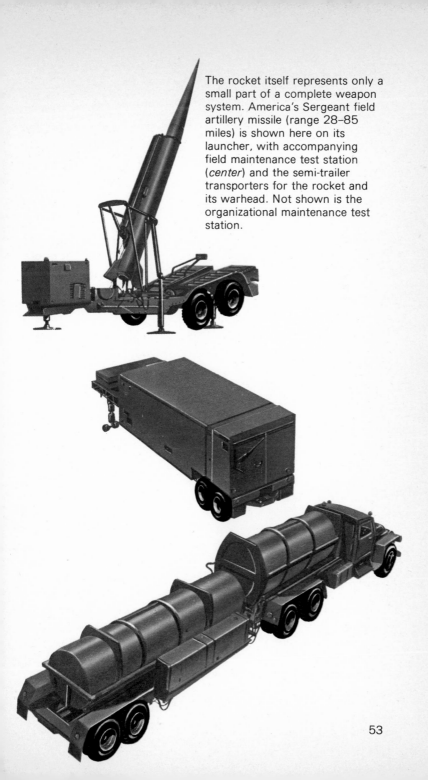

The rocket itself represents only a small part of a complete weapon system. America's Sergeant field artillery missile (range 28–85 miles) is shown here on its launcher, with accompanying field maintenance test station (*center*) and the semi-trailer transporters for the rocket and its warhead. Not shown is the organizational maintenance test station.

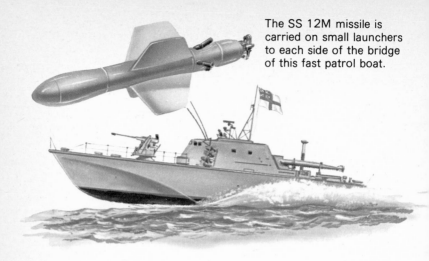

The SS 12M missile is carried on small launchers to each side of the bridge of this fast patrol boat.

Missiles for the navy

The navies of the world have been slower than armies and air forces in switching to missiles for short-range bombardment. Most modern warships carry anti-aircraft missiles; while long-range strategic bombardment missiles like Regulus, Polaris and their Russian counterparts have been in service for many years; but until recently only the Soviet Navy appeared to put any faith in missiles like 'Styx' as replacements for guns for ship-to-ship combat.

Now this situation may change, for several highly efficient, short-range, surface-to-surface naval missiles have been developed and are being evaluated by major navies.

Simplest of them is the Nord SS 12M, a marine version of the wire-guided SS 12/AS 12 (see page 46), which is intended as armament for high-speed coastal and river patrol boats. Two SS 12Ms are carried on a lightweight launcher, which is gyro-stabilized to compensate for movement of the ship and embodies self-contained optical sighting, guidance and control equipment.

In the SS 12M's first demonstration, before representatives of fifteen navies, two missiles were launched from the coastal patrol boat *La Combattante* against a moving target three and a half miles from the ship. Both missiles hit the target within three feet of its center and three feet above the water line.

Hovercraft missile-launcher

Hovercraft appear to offer great advantages as patrol boats and missile-launchers of the future. Since they travel above the surface of the water, they form very stable firing platforms, with far higher speed and better maneuverability than a surface ship.

The illustration below shows a fairly small hovercraft equipped as a launch-platform for America's Sea Lance bombardment missile, which has a range of from three to thirty miles. Such a craft would be able to provide support for amphibious landings by assault forces.

In the type of installation shown, the launchers would be reloaded automatically from below-deck missile stores, using equipment already in production and service for ship-board anti-aircraft missiles. Such standardization reduces costs, as does the fact that Sea Lance is basically similar to the U.S. Army's Lance (see page 50). It has a storable liquid-propellent rocket-engine with twin combustion chambers, a simplified inertial guidance system, and interchangeable nuclear and high-explosive warheads. So far, no one has tried to mount weapons as large as Lance on this type of vehicle, but SS 12Ms have been fired from a small British hovercraft.

Hovercraft offer great possibilities as assault craft, armed with surface-to-surface missiles to soften up the defenses.

Anti-aircraft missiles

The simultaneous appearance of the jet-bomber and the atomic bomb in the last year of World War II posed tremendous new problems for the air defense forces of the world. The first essential was to find a way of dealing with bombers able to fly at heights of fifty thousand feet or more; the answer was the long-range surface-to-air guided missile, working in partnership with missile-armed fighters.

Typical of first-generation anti-aircraft missiles was America's two-stage Nike-Ajax, made up of a liquid-propellent second stage and a solid-propellent first-stage booster. Control was by a radar command system, in which one radar tracked the target while another tracked the missile. A computer worked out the guidance signals necessary to make the two tracks converge, and the missile's high-explosive warhead was detonated by a signal from the ground when the missile was at its closest point to the target.

Russia uses a similar guidance and control system for its 'Guideline' missile which has been widely used in Vietnam.

America's first surface-to-air missile was Nike-Ajax, of which three examples are shown on their ramps.

Russia's 'Ganef' (*left*) and 'Guideline' (*right*). In the center, RAF's Bloodhound.

British Bloodhound and Thunderbird missiles utilize a semi-active homing radar guidance system. In this, a powerful ground radar picks up the target, 'locks' on to it and 'illuminates' it with strong radar beams. These beams 'bounce' back from the target and are picked up by a receiver in the missile which homes on the source of the reflected signals.

Bloodhound is powered by ramjet engines which give it better range than a rocket-motor, and it launched with the aid of four solid-propellent 'wrap-around' boosters, which fall away when burned out. The Russian 'Ganef' has a similar dual power plant and is interesting in that it is carried in pairs on a tracked launcher which gives it great mobility.

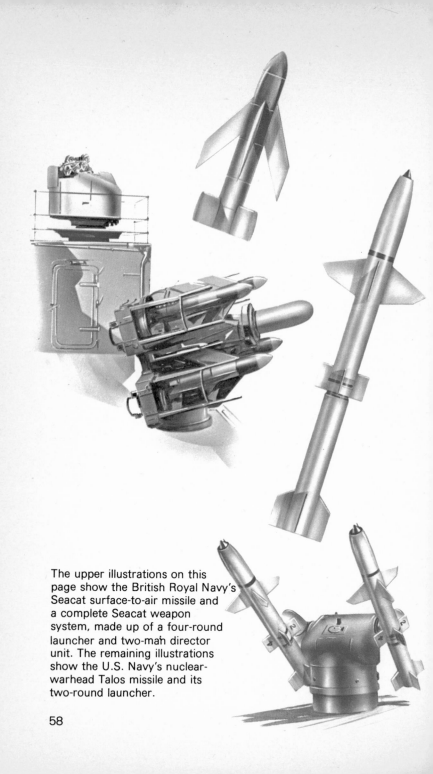

The upper illustrations on this page show the British Royal Navy's Seacat surface-to-air missile and a complete Seacat weapon system, made up of a four-round launcher and two-mah director unit. The remaining illustrations show the U.S. Navy's nuclear-warhead Talos missile and its two-round launcher.

Protection at sea

Designers of naval missiles are always faced by a particular problem, as space is at a premium on board ship and it would be completely impossible to find room for a weapon system as complex as the original Nike-Ajax.

Many first-generation naval surface-to-air missiles, like the American Terrier and Talos and British Seaslug utilize beam-riding guidance, which requires less ground equipment than a command system. The missile flies along a narrow 'pencil beam' of radio signals 'locked' on to the target. As the width of the beam increases with distance, it must be kept as narrow as possible at the transmitter, and a wider 'gathering' beam is often transmitted simultaneously to pick up the missile after launch and direct into the main beam. It is then kept in the main beam by its own radio equipment.

Talos is ramjet-powered, giving it an unusually long slant range (distance from launcher to aircraft in a straight line) of about 65 miles; but most modern ship-launched anti-aircraft missiles have solid-propellent rocket-motors. The ship-board equipment developed for these weapons is very advanced. That installed on the U.S. nuclear-powered cruiser *Long Beach,* for example, embodies an electronic computing center, so that the fire controller can select either a nuclear or high-explosive Talos from below-deck stores, have it extracted, raised to the launcher and fired automatically.

Far simpler is the Seacat, which was designed as a close-range missile to deal with low-flying aircraft or missiles like 'Styx'. It can be fitted to quite small ships and is so efficient that it is deployed by no fewer than fourteen navies.

With the British Royal Navy's Mk 20 Seacat director unit, one man rotates the director so that the second man (the aimer) can pick up the target and follow it through binoculars. The launcher is linked to turn with the director, so that the missile enters the aimer's field of view soon after it is fired. The aimer then steers it to the target by means of a hand control. Alternatively, Seacat can be fired and directed automatically by radar. Soon, Seacat will be supplemented by weapons like the French Exocet, designed to travel more than 20 miles, only 6 to 10 feet above the water, to sink enemy ships before they can launch their 'Styx' type missiles.

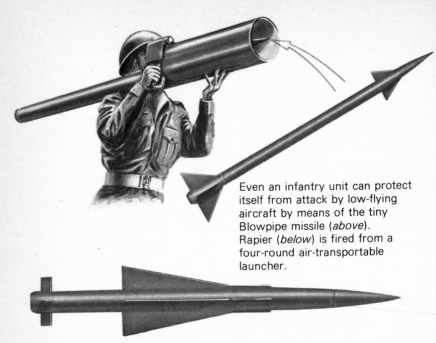

Even an infantry unit can protect itself from attack by low-flying aircraft by means of the tiny Blowpipe missile (*above*). Rapier (*below*) is fired from a four-round air-transportable launcher.

Low-down weapons

Surface-to-air missiles are so efficient at high altitudes that strategic bombing forces have had to change their tactics. The use of air-to-surface stand-off missiles partly solved the problem, as the range of anti-aircraft missiles is quite short, varying from about twenty-five miles for 'Guideline' to sixty-five miles for the American ramjet-powered Talos. An alternative is to fly very low, as it takes time for the guidance system to pick up a missile and begin controlling it after launch, with the result that a weapon like 'Guideline' is of no use against aircraft flying at tree-top height. However, by forcing aircraft to fly low, it brings them with range of predicted anti-aircraft gunfire.

Completely new types of missiles have had to be evolved to deal with the threat of low-flying bombers. One of the first was the American Hawk, for which a special semi-active radar guidance system was developed that could distinguish a moving target at low altitude from a mass of signals reflected from buildings, hills or trees. Hawk became the first missile to destroy a ballistic rocket when it intercepted an Honest John.

Short Brothers and Harland, in Britain, have produced a remarkable anti-aircraft weapon system called Blowpipe, which can be carried and fired by one man. It consists only of the missile, housed in a canister which serves as a launch-tube, and an aiming unit attached to the canister. The missile can be prepared for action in twenty seconds and is guided to the target by means of binoculars and a thumb control.

Blowpipe is intended to protect front-line troops from attack by enemy fighter-bombers in places where no other anti-aircraft protection can be provided. Hardly less mobile is the British Rapier, a low-cost weapon system that can deal with helicopters, subsonic and supersonic aircraft from near ground level to heights up to about ten thousand feet. Four Rapiers and their radar equipment are carried on a light-weight trailer that can be towed by a Land Rover or carried by small aircraft and helicopters. The one-man fire-control unit and spare missiles are carried on board the Land Rover. The first version of Rapier is visually steered, but later models will be radar guided and so will be suitable for use by day and night in all weathers.

America's Hawk is shown here on its latest three-round self-propelled launcher.

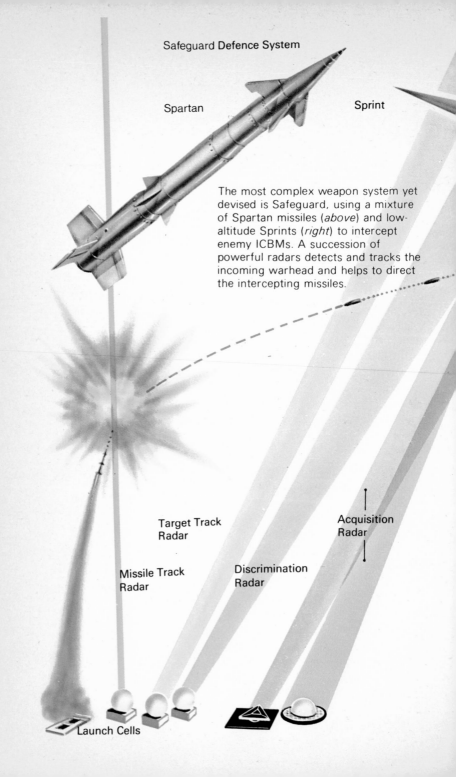

Safeguard Defence System

Spartan

Sprint

The most complex weapon system yet devised is Safeguard, using a mixture of Spartan missiles (*above*) and low-altitude Sprints (*right*) to intercept enemy ICBMs. A succession of powerful radars detects and tracks the incoming warhead and helps to direct the intercepting missiles.

Target Track Radar

Acquisition Radar

Missile Track Radar

Discrimination Radar

Launch Cells

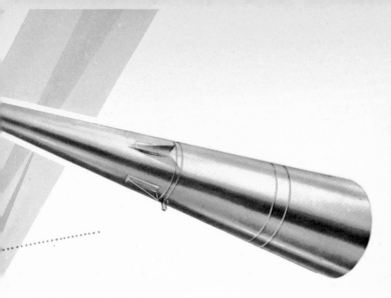

Anti-missile missiles

At the other extreme from the one-man Blowpipe are the anti-missile missile systems now being installed in both the United States and Russia. Little is known about the Soviet weapon, as the missile (known to NATO as 'Galosh') has been seen only inside its transport container; but it could hardly be less complex than the American Safeguard in view of the vast problems involved in detecting and intercepting a tiny ICBM warhead re-entering the atmosphere at around 15,000 mph, especially when the warhead is protected by decoys.

A small-scale deployment of Safeguard, intended to protect Minuteman sites against enemy missiles, is expected to cost $5 billion.

Huge BMEWS (Ballistic Missile Early Warning System) radar antennae in Greenland, England and Alaska were set up originally to detect the launch of Russian missiles. They will be replaced eventually by satellites able to detect launchings anywhere in the world. Once alerted that a missile had been fired, target acquisition radars would begin searching for the incoming warhead. Within seconds of its location, a Safeguard battery would be assigned to its interception. Tracking radars would 'lock' on to the warhead as it came within range, passing data to a high-speed computer which would calculate and transmit signals to guide a long-range Spartan or short-range Sprint missile on an interception course.

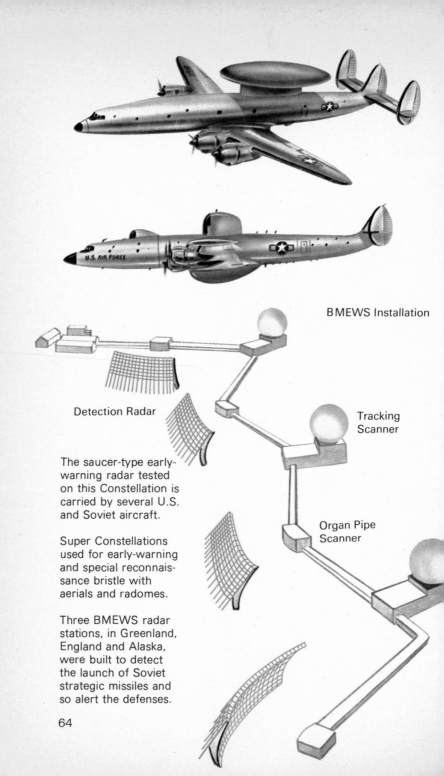

BMEWS Installation

Detection Radar

Tracking
Scanner

Organ Pipe
Scanner

The saucer-type early-
warning radar tested
on this Constellation is
carried by several U.S.
and Soviet aircraft.

Super Constellations
used for early-warning
and special reconnais-
sance bristle with
aerials and radomes.

Three BMEWS radar
stations, in Greenland,
England and Alaska,
were built to detect
the launch of Soviet
strategic missiles and
so alert the defenses.

Part of the defense against manned bombers—the missile-armed F-106 Delta Dart.

An integrated defense system

Costly though it is, an anti-missile missile system represents only a small item in the integrated defense network that is needed today to protect a nation against all forms of attack.

For many years now, the United States and Canada have been defended by such a network, operated by NORAD (North American Air Defense Command). Intended to deal with attacks by aircraft and missiles other than the ballistic type, NORAD's defense network uses the BMEWS radar sites and radar chains stretching right across Canada and the United States to provide early warning of an attack. They are supplemented by early-warning aircraft, carrying radar scanners in huge blisters and 'saucers', designed to detect aircraft, missiles and ships that might slip through in sectors not covered by the surface radar.

Any unidentified aircraft detected by radar is investigated by a missile-armed fighter—a practice that has alarmed more than one pilot cruising along peacefully in one of the larger and faster types of private business aircraft!

All United States and Canadian fighter and missile defenses are controlled by the SAGE (Semi-Automatic Ground Environment) network of underground control posts, the primary duty of which is to ensure that no target is overlooked and no interception duplicated. SAGE decides whether a threat should be countered by fighters or missiles, and which air force base or missile site is best positioned to do the job. Fighter pilots are guided by radar toward their target until they are close enough for the automatic search and fire-control radar system carried in the nose of their aircraft to take over for the final stage of interception.

Minimizing the man

Modern air combat is no man-to-man affair between knights in shining armor. It is fought by electronic black boxes and guided missiles, with men present to take over only if the machines fail.

A typical interception sortie might begin with the detection by radar of an unidentified aircraft approaching at 1,000 mph at a height of 50,000 feet. The signal to take off and investigate is flashed to a pilot at stand-by alert in the cockpit of his fighter. Within seconds, he slams shut the cockpit hood, starts the en-

A few of the wide range of air-to-air missiles in current use are illustrated on these and the next two pages, with four of the fighters that carry them.

A. The infra-red homing Red Top, carried by Lightning interceptors.
B. The infra-red Sidewinder homes on heat emitted by the engines of an enemy aircraft.
C. In addition to this infra-red homing Falcon, there is a radar homing version.
D. Standard Soviet air-to-air missile is 'Anab': radar-homing and infra-red versions are carried in pairs.
E. First nuclear-warhead air-to-air missile was the unguided Genie rocket.
F. The semi-active radar homing version of the Matra R.530, carried by the French Mirage.
G. Not yet in production, the YF-12A is a 2,000-mph interceptor with long-range Falcon missiles housed in internal bays.
H. The Phantom carries Sparrow missiles under its fuselage.

G

H

gine of his aircraft and races along the runway and up into the air, with white-hot exhaust gases blasting from the nozzle of the reheated jet-engine.

Radio signals tell him what course to steer as he climbs at the rate of nearly 50,000 feet a minute. As he closes on the unidentified aircraft, he is told to switch over to the fire-control radar system in the nose of his fighter. From that moment he is no more than a passenger. At night he might never even see the aircraft he is to intercept, except as a blip on the radar screen in his cockpit.

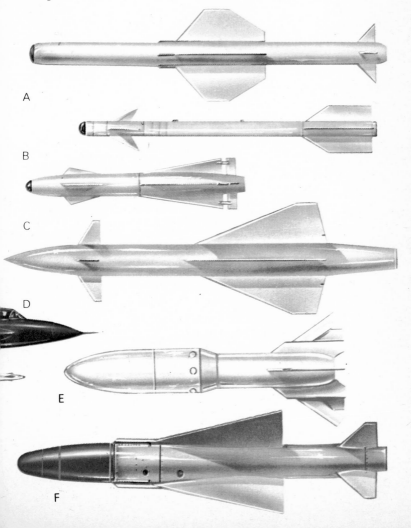

A

B

C

D

E

F

Sea Vixen fighters of the British Navy can carry either Firestreak (illustrated) or Red Top infra-red missiles.

Yak-28 of the Soviet Air Force, armed with two underwing 'Anab' missiles.

If it were wartime, the radar would 'lock' on to the target and fly the fighter automatically toward it, while identification radar 'interrogated' the aircraft to discover if it were friend or foe. If the answer appeared to be 'hostile', and ground control confirmed that an attack should be made, the radar would guide the fighter to within range of the target, fire its missiles automatically at the best possible moment to ensure success and then break off the engagement by turning the fighter for home. The pilot would then resume control for the return to base.

Air-to-air missiles
The illustrations on these and the two previous pages show a number of typical modern air-to-air weapons and the various ways in which they are carried by interceptor fighters. Although small, one or two of them carry nuclear warheads.

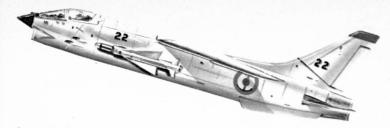

Crusader fighters of the French Navy carry an R.530 missile on each side of their fuselage.

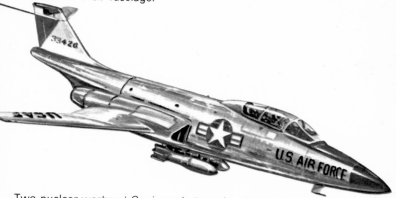

Two nuclear-warhead Genie rockets under the fuselage of an F-101B Voodoo fighter.

Several different types of guidance systems are used in air-to-air missiles, including beam-riding and fully-active homing, in which the missile homes on signals transmitted by radar in its nose and reflected from the target. The most common forms of air-to-air guidance are, however, semi-active radar homing and infra-red homing.

Semi-active systems work in exactly the same way as those utilized in surface-to-air weapon systems (see page 57), with the radar transmitter housed in the nose of the fighter from which the missile is launched.

Infra-red guidance is known as a 'passive' system, as no signals are transmitted by the missile or its launch aircraft. Instead, a sensitive device located behind the nose of the missile detects the heat from the engine exhaust of the enemy aircraft, over a very long range, and homes in on the source of the heat.

69

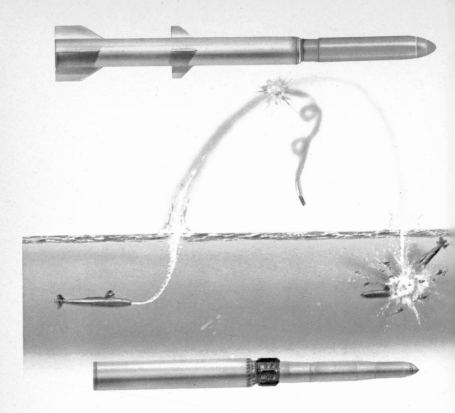

Anti-submarine missiles of the United States include the surface-launched Asroc (*top*) and submarine-launched Subroc (*bottom*).

No hiding place

In two World Wars, German U-boats came close to bringing Britain to her knees, by closing her sea supply routes. The modern nuclear submarine is infinitely more formidable, being able to remain submerged indefinitely, cruise at speeds as great as surface warships and launch missiles like Polaris which could remove a whole city from the map. Today, not even the sea offers a secure hiding place. There are ways of detecting even a submerged submarine and weapons able to seek it out and destroy it.

One of the simplest is the U.S. Navy's Asroc (anti-submarine rocket). Housed in a multiple launcher, it is aimed very accurately by a computer which uses data obtained from the ship's sonar to work out the course, range and speed of the submarine. When launched, Asroc follows a ballistic trajectory. On receipt of a signal from the ship, it sheds its motor and airframe. If its payload is a torpedo, this is lowered by parachute into the water and then homes automatically on the submarine. When Asroc carries a nuclear depth charge, this sinks to a predetermined depth and then detonates with sufficient force to sink any submarine within a very wide radius.

Subroc (submarine rocket) works in a similar way, but is launched from the standard torpedo tubes of a submarine, has an inertial guidance system to make it accurate over ranges as great as thirty miles, and always carries a nuclear depth-bomb warhead. Operational since 1965, it will eventually equip about twenty-five fast nuclear attack submarines.

The way in which the French Navy's Malafon anti-submarine missile works is shown in the diagram below.

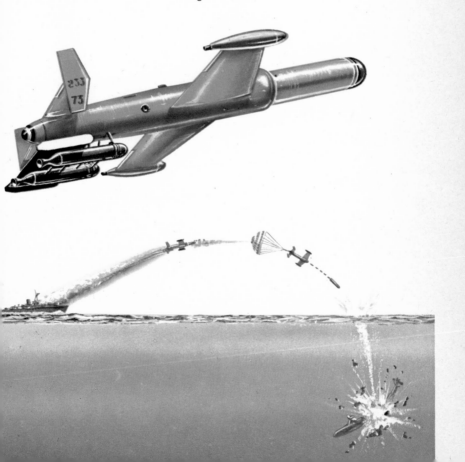

Titan II   Atlas   Burned-out Atlas boosters falling away.

Very different is the French Malafon, a flying-bomb built around a 21-inch torpedo which homes on to the sound made by a submarine's engines. Malafon is launched from a ship-board ramp with the aid of two solid-propellent boosters which accelerate it to 515 mph in three seconds. They then fall away and the rest of the flight is unpowered.

Malafon is kept at a constant height of 330 feet above the sea by a radar altimeter, which also adjusts the incidence of the wings to provide increased lift as the missile's forward speed decreases. The ship's sonar continues to track the target and steer the missile toward it by radio command. About half a mile from the target, the missile is slowed by a tail parachute; the torpedo is shot forward from its nose by inertia, enters the water, and homes on the submarine. Malafon will equip thirteen ships of the French Navy.

The ultimate weapon

Throughout history, politicians and military men have dreamed of producing the ultimate weapon which would enable them to conquer the whole world. With the ICBM (inter-continental ballistic missile) we may have the ultimate weapon, for the thermonuclear (H-bomb) warheads carried by rockets already in service in the United States and Russia are more than adequate to remove all life from huge areas of the globe. However, their effect has been to bring not world conquest but an uneasy freedom from world war, as they are too terrible for anyone but a nation bent on suicide to use.

All of the ICBMs illustrated on these two pages are, or were, inertially guided multi-stage liquid-propellent rockets with a range of at least five thousand miles.

The American Atlas, now retired from military use and employed as a satellite launcher, differs from the others in that all its motors fire together at launch. They consist of a main (sustainer) engine, flanked by two boosters, with two small vernier motors mounted at ninety degrees to the boosters.

These two large Soviet ICBMs, 'Scrag' (*left*) and 'Sasin', are not thought to have entered service.

In the Atlas ICBM, the burned-out boosters were jettisoned about 120 seconds after blast-off, taking with them the flared skirt around the base of the missile. The sustainer engine shut down four and a half minutes after launch, leaving the verniers to adjust the missile's speed precisely for the required range. After vernier shut-down, the missile followed an unguided ballistic trajectory. Its warhead was separated by retro-rockets and traveled on by itself in a high arc before re-entering the atomsphere over the target.

The American Titan and Russian 'Scrag' and 'Sasin' are more orthodox, in that their later stages begin firing after the first ones have burned out and fallen away.

Atlas was designed to be fired from 'soft' above-ground launch-pads, which made it vulnerable to attack. It was adapted for horizontal stowage in 'semi-hard' concrete boxes, but the only satisfactory way of protecting ICBMs is to store them underground in concrete pits known as silos. Titan I had to be elevated clear of its silo for launch; but Titan II can be launched from underground 'hard' sites.

Controlling the deterrent

A deterrent force is effective only if it is seen to be so destructive and so certain to get through to its target that no nation dares to start a major war. That is why the United States and Russia had to bury their ICBMs in underground silos, safe from surprise attack. The process was made easier for the United States by the perfection of powerful new solid-propellent rocket motors which enabled the Air Force to replace its huge liquid-propellent Atlas and Titan missiles with the smaller three-stage solid-propellent Minuteman.

Although Minuteman II is only 59 feet 10 inches long, compared with the 115-foot Titan II, and weighs only 70,000 pounds compared with 330,000 pounds, it will carry a ther-

monuclear warhead over a range of more than 7,000 miles. It utilizes an inertial guidance system and, like all solid-propellent missiles, is always ready for immediate launching.

There are 1,000 Minuteman missiles, deployed underground at six Air Force bases in Montana, North and South Dakota, Missouri and Wyoming. Each silo launcher is about eighty feet deep and twelve feet in diameter, with two underground equipment rooms around the silo casing, extending some twenty-eight feet below the surface.

Each flight of ten launchers is served by a launch control center in the form of a blast-proof capsule about fifty feet underground, manned by two Strategic Air Command officers. To ensure control of the deterrent even if all underground posts were put out of action, the entire Minuteman force could be launched from airborne launch control centers in modified EC-135 aircraft.

(*Opposite page*) EC-135C airborne launch control center. (*Right*) Minuteman solid-propellent ICBM in its launch silo.

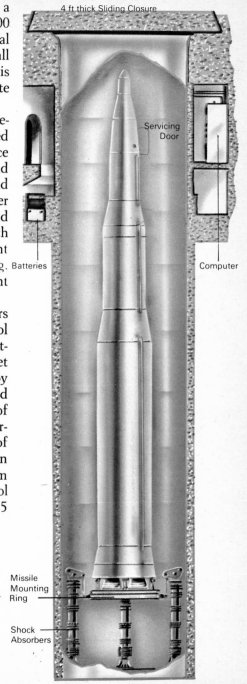

4 ft thick Sliding Closure

Servicing Door

Batteries

Computer

Missile Mounting Ring

Shock Absorbers

The new capital ships

Even when missiles like Minuteman are stored in underground launch sites, there is always the possibility that some way might be found of putting them out of action. The task of the enemy defenses is also made easier by the fact that the positions of the launch sites are known. This is why the United States government decided to send part of its deterrent force of nuclear-warhead missiles to sea—in submarines that would be harder to pinpoint and which could launch an attack from virtually anywhere in the oceans that cover nearly three-quarters of the Earth's surface.

Today, the U.S. Navy has forty-one nuclear-powered missile submarines in service, each carrying sixteen Polaris mis-

This drawing of a U.S. missile
submarine is cut away to show
the 16 Polaris A2 missiles in
their vertical launch-tubes.
Smaller drawings show Polaris
A2 and its French equivalent, the
MSBS (*below*) and
Polaris A3 (*opposite page*).

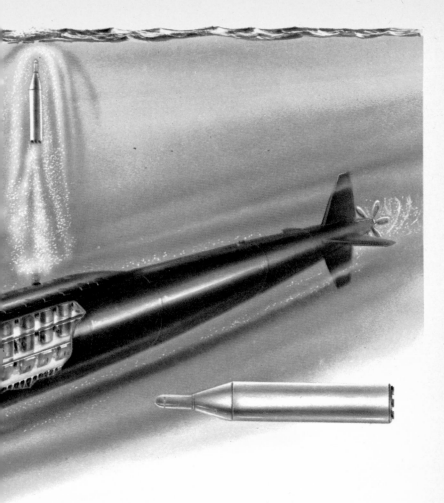

siles. Twenty-eight of the ships carry the Polaris A3, with a range of 2,875 miles; the others are armed with the 1,700-mile range Polaris A2. The A3 also equips four submarines of Britain's Royal Navy, and both Russia and France operate missile submarines carrying somewhat similar weapons.

Polaris is a two-stage solid-propellent missile with an inertial guidance system. It is 'popped' from its launch-tube by exhaust gas from a small rocket in the submarine, its own first-stage motor firing only as it leaves the water. It is to be superseded in many of the American submarines by the larger Poseidon, with a multiple warhead containing decoys to confuse the enemy's defense system.

ROCKETS INTO SPACE

By perfecting the V-2 rocket in World War II, the Germans not only ushered in the era of push-button weapons but put mankind firmly upon the road that has led to exploration of the Moon and planets of our solar system.

V-2 itself was used in both the United States and Russia as a sounding vehicle to carry scientific instruments into the upper layers of Earth's atmosphere. Useful information was obtained from these flights, the main snag being that V-2 became unstable and tumbled when its motor stopped running, which limited the volume of data that it could radio back to the ground. In any case, the supply of V-2s was soon exhausted.

Excited by the prospect of learning quickly far more about the upper atmosphere than had been possible in the whole of recorded history, United States scientists set out their requirements for a series of basic research rockets. One result was the simple liquid-propellent Aerobee which, when launched by a solid-propellent booster, could carry 75 pounds of instru-

The Russian A-2 research rocket (*above*), and the equipment container of Russia's big A-3 research rocket.

ments to a height of 75 miles.

Aerobee was one of the first of the whole vast range of sounding rockets that are used throughout the world today for meteorological and other research, at heights of up to two thousand miles. Most send back information by radio telemetry, but some release chemical clouds or radar-reflective chaff for measurement of wind speeds, while others have a detachable instrument package that can be retrieved by parachute. Despite the comparative simplicity of the early sounding rockets, they achieved some remarkable results. . Aerobee, for example, showed for the first time what a hurricane looks like from above.

More ambitious than Aerobee was the Viking rocket developed for the U.S. Naval Research Laboratory by the Martin company. It drew heavily on V-2 technology, but its 20,000 pound thrust liquid oxygen/alcohol engine was the most advanced built in America up to that time and it proved tremendously successful.

79

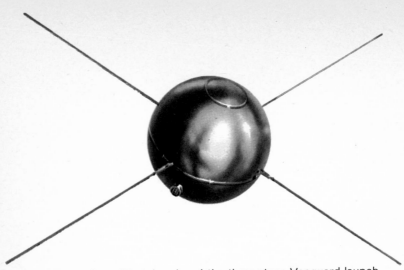

Vanguard satellite (*above*) and the three-stage Vanguard launch vehicle (*below*).

Viking 1, launched on May 3, 1949, climbed to a height of 50 miles; Viking 4 reached 105 miles; and Viking 11 set up a record of 158 miles, carrying 852 pounds of instruments. Of the fourteen Vikings built, only one was a failure—and then only because it broke free of its tie-downs while its power plant was undergoing a static test.

Elated by the success of its first big rocket, the United States decided to mark the 1957 International Geophysical Year by attempting something that rocket enthusiasts had dreamed of for years. Viking had sent back the first photographs of the Earth from heights so great that the curvature of the horizon was visible. Its successor, Vanguard, was to attempt to put an instrumented satellite into orbit around the Earth, to overcome the main drawback of research rockets—the brief period of time during which they are able to send back data in flight. Although less-publicized, the Russians had also agreed to attempt a satellite launching.

The United States had three choices of launch vehicle in the 1957 International Geophysical year. Rejection of the first of these, the Atlas ICBM, was understandable, as it was an unproven design. Less logical was the refusal to add an extra stage to Jupiter-C, a version of Redstone, which demonstrated its capability by projecting a payload 3,400 miles over the Atlantic in September 1956.

The committee set up to plan the project chose to develop an entirely new rocket, named Vanguard, utilizing experience gained with the Viking. They argued that success was more likely if the launcher was designed especially for the job and that it would make no demands on von Braun and his colleagues at Redstone Arsenal, who were heavily engaged on military projects.

Meanwhile, Russia had begun adapting one of its big military rockets to carry a satellite named Sputnik I. Working on the rule-of-thumb basis that every pound of satellite needed 1,000 pounds of rocket to put it into orbit, the Vanguard rocket was designed as a three-stage vehicle, 72 feet long and with a weight of 22,600 pounds. Its satellite was to be a 20-inch sphere weighing a mere 21 pounds.

On October 4, 1957, before the first Vanguard was ready for test, with a powered first stage and dummy upper stages, Russia put Sputnik I into orbit, thereby winning the first lap of what the press began to refer to as the 'space race'.

Although bitterly disappointed, the United States derived some consolation when the first Vanguard test vehicle made a successful flight on October 23, 1957. The second rocket, with all stages powered, exploded on its launch pad. The third broke up at a height of less than four miles. In despair, the designers built a 3¼ pound 'grapefruit' satellite, put it on board the fourth Vanguard and, at last, had the satisfaction of seeing their rocket put this tiny sphere into orbit on March 17, 1958.

By then, however, Russia had progressed to putting the first living creature into orbit (the dog Laika). On January 31, 1958, the United States put its first satellite, an 18-pound satellite named Explorer I, into orbit with a modified Jupiter-C rocket, to measure cosmic rays, micrometeorites and temperatures in space.

The first satellites

Sputnik I, the world's first artificial satellite, took about ninety-six minutes to encircle the Earth, in an elliptical orbit with an apogee (furthest point from Earth) of 588 miles and perigee (nearest point) of 142 miles. This perigee brought it within the fringes of the atmosphere, which slowed it a little on each orbit, so that it fell back to Earth and burned up on January 4, 1958. By comparison, America's little Vanguard I, with a perigee of 409 miles, should survive 1,000 years.

Both of these satellites carried radio transmitters to send back information on conditions in space; but from the start the public was more interested in the possibility of space travel. For this reason, Sputnik II, launched on November 3, 1957, created even more of a sensation, for its payload included a dog named Laika.

In addition to Laika's pressurized container, this satellite carried several groups of scientific instruments. The whole assembly weighed a staggering half-ton.

Russia's Sputnik I, Sputnik II and Sputnik III satellites.

The first living
creature put into orbit
was the dog Laika
carried by Sputnik II.
Many other dogs have
taken part in Soviet space
research programs;
these drawings show a
typical life support capsule
used in such flights.

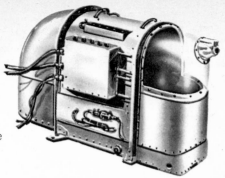

External view of Capsule Kennel

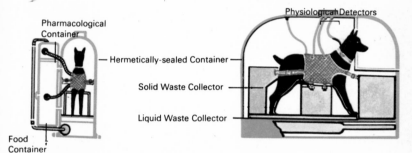

Pharmacological
Container

— Hermetically-sealed Container —

Solid Waste Collector

Liquid Waste Collector

Physiological Detectors

Food
Container

For eight days the little dog encircled the Earth with no apparent ill-effects. Measurement of her heartbeats, temperature and other conditions were telemetered continuously to Earth until, on November 11, they suddenly ceased. Nobody at that time had learned to recover an object from orbit and Laika had been put to death painlessly, her work completed.

What would the Russians do next? The answer came on May 15, 1958, when Sputnik III went into orbit. With a length of 11 feet 7 inches, it was a cone-shaped flying laboratory weighing 2,926 pounds, including nearly a ton of scientific instruments, radio and batteries.

We know now that Russia's early successes in space resulted from the fact that her nuclear warheads were so bulky that huge rockets were needed to carry them. Having these huge military rockets, Russia was able to adapt them for her satellite launch program and could thus build much larger satellites than those planned for the United States' small Vanguard rocket. This superiority in size was challenged by the larger number of United States' satellites soon to be launched.

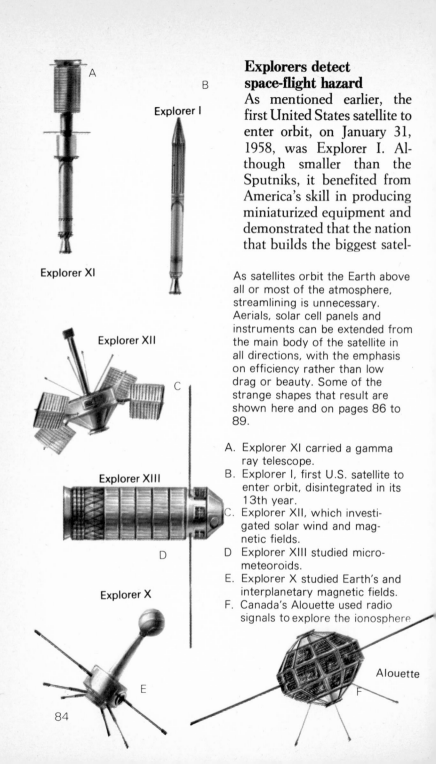

Explorers detect space-flight hazard

As mentioned earlier, the first United States satellite to enter orbit, on January 31, 1958, was Explorer I. Although smaller than the Sputniks, it benefited from America's skill in producing miniaturized equipment and demonstrated that the nation that builds the biggest satel-

As satellites orbit the Earth above all or most of the atmosphere, streamlining is unnecessary. Aerials, solar cell panels and instruments can be extended from the main body of the satellite in all directions, with the emphasis on efficiency rather than low drag or beauty. Some of the strange shapes that result are shown here and on pages 86 to 89.

A. Explorer XI carried a gamma ray telescope.
B. Explorer I, first U.S. satellite to enter orbit, disintegrated in its 13th year.
C. Explorer XII, which investigated solar wind and magnetic fields.
D Explorer XIII studied micrometeoroids.
E. Explorer X studied Earth's and interplanetary magnetic fields.
F. Canada's Alouette used radio signals to explore the ionosphere

Explorer XI

Explorer I

Explorer XII

Explorer XIII

Explorer X

Alouette

lites does not necessarily derive the greatest benefits in terms of scientific discovery.

Data telemetered from Sputnik II and its passenger had implied that the danger to life from cosmic and solar radiation while in orbit was negligible. Explorer I told a different story. As it approached its apogee of 1,590 miles, considerably further from Earth than its predecessors had traveled, the Geiger tubes put aboard by Dr. James Van Allen to measure radiation suddenly went out of action.

Van Allen concluded that they had been saturated by very intense radiation, and this was confirmed in July 1958 by Explorer IV. Further measurements of great value were obtained from the Pioneer I probe, which traveled 70,000 miles into space; but it was Explorer XII that finally revealed the true extent of the hazard. During 102 highly eccentric orbits, with an apogee of 48,000 miles and perigee of 182 miles, it crossed and recrossed what had become known as the Van Allen radiation belts and sent back 2,500 miles of tape-recorded data. These showed that there is really one big belt of charged radiation particles that have been trapped by the Earth's magnetic field, shaped like a 'hole-in-the-middle' doughnut and leaving relatively clear areas over the North and South Poles. The belt extends from a height of a few hundred miles to a distance of nearly 45,000 miles from the Earth, with the most dangerous regions at heights of around 2,000 and 12,000 miles. Clearly, the science-fiction writers who had written about lethal radiation in space were better prophets than they realized.

As the scientific space explorers became more confident of putting their payloads into orbit without difficulty, the shapes of the satellites changed from simple spheres and cones into a variety of forms. With little or no atmosphere to create drag, it was possible to have panels of solar cells on 'paddles' projecting from the main structure in the way best calculated to catch the sunlight, which was then converted by the cells into new life for the satellite's batteries. Instrumentation packages, too, could be spread out around the body on stalks, and aerials that unwound like a spring-steel rule were soon extending up to 120 feet on each side of some satellites to improve measurements or telemetry.

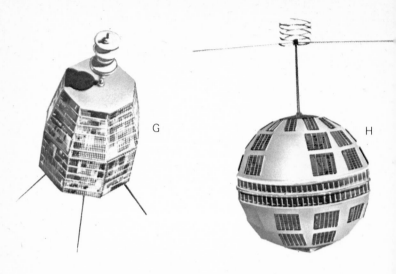

G

H

Satellites become commercial

The man in the street could understand the significance of the
Van Allen radiation belts, because they represented a danger
to the life of human space travelers; but most of the information
sent back by early satellites was concerned with pure research
into phenomena such as atmospheric density, temperature and
pressure, magnetic fields and micrometeorites, solar and cosmic radiation and geodesy, the study of the Earth's shape.

It was learned that the Earth was less symmetrical and that
the air at a height of 150 miles was denser than previously assumed. However, these discoveries did not affect daily life and
seemed remote to many who followed the space achievements.

The satellite that made them change their minds was Telstar, which relayed the first live television pictures across the
Atlantic, enabling viewers in Europe to watch events in America as they were happening. Before long, intercontinental television became accepted as a routine wonder of the space age,
the satellites being built and orbited as commercial ventures
by private companies who recouped the expense by charging
for the relay service.

86

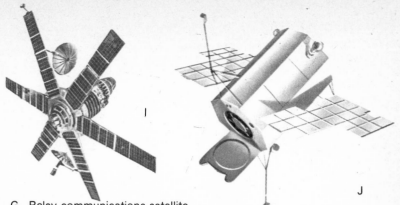

G. Relay communications satellite.
H. Telstar made possible the first transatlantic TV.
I. Russia's Molniya communications satellite.
J. OAO, the Orbiting Astronomical Observatory.

Early relay satellites could be used only during the periods of their orbit when they were in the right position to pass television pictures between continents. To ensure a 24-hour continuous service, it was necessary to put the satellites into what is called a synchronous orbit. This is easy to explain:

The further from Earth a satellite is placed, the longer it takes to complete each orbit. Thus, when it is put into a perfectly circular orbit 22,300 miles above the Earth, it takes just 24 hours to make each circuit. If the orbit is parallel with the equator the satellite stays permanently over a particular spot on the surface, because the Earth also takes 24 hours to make one complete rotation on its axis. Just three satellites equi-spaced around the equator in such a synchronous orbit can provide a permanent television relay service between any points on the Earth's surface.

Many communications satellites are now in orbit, to provide such services. Typical examples are the Intelsat III and the Russian Molniya satellites produced by a consortium of companies in seven countries. Intelsat III weighs 608 pounds and can handle 1,200 telephone calls or four television channels. By mid-1969, Intelsat III's had been put into synchronous orbit over the Atlantic, Pacific and Indian Oceans, to serve more than forty-five countries. The bigger Intelsat IV will provide 5,000 telephone and twelve simultaneous color television channels.

K   L

Forecasting weather and war

Few people realize what an immense variety of jobs are being performed by satellites today. For example, the feat of the Aerobee which photographed a complete hurricane is now routine for meteorological satellites, which provide a day and night picture of cloud cover over the Earth, making possible more accurate weather forecasting.

For centuries, astronomers have dreamed of being able to put a telescope above the Earth's atmosphere, which distorts and destroys in milli-seconds light waves that have taken thousands of years to travel through space. The huge American OAO (orbiting astronomical observatory) satellite is designed to do just that.

Satellites are used for spying, as well as for peaceful scientific research. Both the United States and Russia utilize 'spy' satellites for reconnaissance flights, to photograph military installations and learn about each other's radar progress by means of ingenious electronic devices. Data from such satellites is not only telemetered to Earth. The USAF has evolved an ingenious 'air snatch' technique by which reconnaissance capsules can be ejected from satellites and retrieved in mid-air as they float down by parachute.

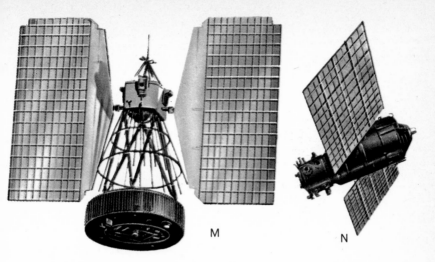

K. Early Bird, the first commercial communications satellite.
L. Russia's giant 12-ton Proton satellite was built to study high-energy cosmic particles.
M. The American Nimbus.
N The Russian Cosmos 144. Both are successful meteorological satellites.

Diagram of the 'air snatch' technique used by the USAF to recover reconnaissance satellites.

Menagerie in space

Before the United States or Russia succeeded in putting a man into space, a cartoon in a Dutch magazine depicted what it called 'The crew room at Cape Canaveral'. In this imaginary room at America's space flight center was a menagerie of mice, dogs and monkeys, sipping beer and swopping yarns.

This was fair comment. Laika had been followed into space by several more dogs in Russian research rockets, and they were recovered none the worse for their exploits. The United States sent monkeys, in the belief that these comparatively intelligent creatures would react more like humans and could even be trained to perform simple tests in orbit.

There was nothing new in all this. The first living creatures to leave the Earth in an aircraft—a Montgolfier hot-air balloon—in September 1783, had been a sheep, a cock and a duck. Nor was it particularly callous. Except in the case of Laika, there was every chance that the animals would survive their experience and they were outfitted as carefully as any human astronaut, with a pressurized spacesuit, safety harness, oxygen, food and water.

First living creatures to leave the Earth in an aircraft were a sheep, a cock and a duck in a basket under a hot-air balloon (*opposite page*). Animal passengers in rockets, like this rhesus monkey (*left*), paved the way for humans to follow.

In 1959, the Americans recovered two small Rhesus monkeys after a 1,500-mile flight through space in a Jupiter missile nose-cone. They followed this achievement on January 31, 1961 by sending a chimpanzee named Ham on an entirely successful trip to a height of 155 miles in one of the Mercury spacecraft which they had designed as vehicles for their first man-in-space program.

By then, however, the Russians were also very much in the race. Unlike the Americans, who had kept the public informed concerning every aspect of the Mercury project, they revealed little beyond the fact that the 4½-ton 'spaceship satellite' Sputnik V had been recovered safely from orbit on August 20, 1960, carrying two dogs, twelve mice, insects, plants, cultures of fungi, seeds, microbes and other biological specimens. It was clearly only a matter of time before the first man followed them.

MEN INTO SPACE

The first spaceman

On April 12, 1961, a twenty-seven-year-old Russian, Major Yuri Alekseyevich Gagarin, became the first man to circle the Earth in orbital flight.

The Americans had decided to precede orbital launches of their Mercury spacecraft with a series of up-and-down sub-orbital flights in a ballistic trajectory over the Atlantic. The Russians had such confidence in their huge launch rockets and their much simpler spacecraft, which they called the Vostok I, that their very first manned flight was aimed into Earth orbit.

When they announced the successful recovery of Vostok I after a single orbit, lasting I hour 48 minutes, they stated that the spacecraft weighed 10,418 pounds and consisted of the pilot's capsule, with

Russia's mighty Vostok launch vehicle which put Major Yuri Gagarin into orbit on April 12, 1961.
(*Opposite page*) the flight path of Major Gagarin's single-orbit flight, starting from Tyuratam (Baikonur) cosmodrome and ending in a plowed field near the village of Saratov.

landing system, and a separate section carrying the instrumentation and retro-rocket. No indication was given of the shape or size of the craft, and the only photographs that were released showed it hidden inside what was obviously a pointed rocket nose fairing with a diameter of about 8 feet 6 inches.

Not until the summer of 1967 was the appearance of the Vostok launcher revealed, in the shape of a full-size replica, at the Paris Air Show. More than 124 feet tall, the Vostok launcher was made up of a two-stage central core vehicle, with four tapered booster rockets mounted around the lower part of the first stage. All rockets were of the liquid-propellent type, with four primary nozzles and two verniers on each booster and four primary nozzles and four verniers on the first-stage engine. Thus, no fewer than thirty-two rocket chambers were fired simultaneously at take-off, giving a total thrust of more than one million pounds.

It was in a small capsule perched high on the nose of this mighty rocket that Yuri Gagarin had set out, just after nine o'clock on the morning of April 12, 1961, on the voyage that was to write his name forever in the world's history books.

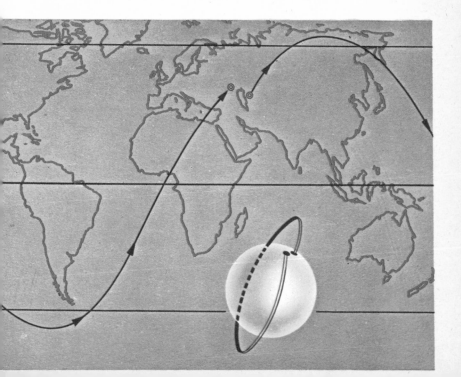

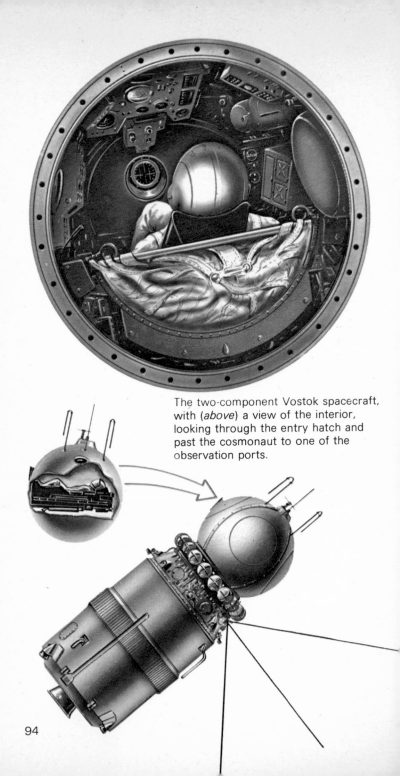

The two-component Vostok spacecraft,
with (*above*) a view of the interior,
looking through the entry hatch and
past the cosmonaut to one of the
observation ports.

The Vostok spacecraft

The public had its first sight of Gagarin's capsule at the Soviet Economic Achievement Exhibition in Moscow in April 1965.

As stated by the Russians in 1961, it consisted of two components, carried on the nose of the second stage of the launch vehicle. The overall length of the complete assembly was 24 feet 1½ inches, excluding the aerials projecting from it.

Perhaps the most surpising feature of the spacecraft was the simplicity of the capsule housing the cosmonaut's cabin. It proved to be a sphere with a diameter of 7 feet 6½ inches. Instead of utilizing a control system to ensure that the capsule would re-enter the Earth's atmosphere in the correct attitude, the Russian designers simply put a greater thickness of heat-shielding material on the side that had to re-enter first, the resulting offset position of the center of gravity ensuring that it would do so automatically.

Gagarin lay in an ejection seat, mounted on rails and embodying the spacesuit ventilation system. To his left were a control panel, drinking water supply, emergency heat regulation system, landing system radar, a tape recorder and the container for the capsule's landing parachute.

On the right of the cabin were the manual control stick, food supply, air-regeneration equipment, clock, radio, sanitary system and the television camera which gave viewers in the Soviet Union a picture of the cosmonaut in orbit.

The instrument section, between the capsule and the second-stage rocket, contained the orientation system and fuel supply, oxygen and air containers, electric power units, retrorockets and radio and telemetry equipment.

Four small engines mounted around the rear of the second-stage casing were used to steer Vostok I into the required orbit, after which the complete second stage was jettisoned. For re-entry, the spacecraft was orientated automatically by a device which used as its reference the position of the sun. The retro-rocket was then fired, after which the instrument section was jettisoned. During re-entry, Gagarin reclined across the craft, taking the deceleration loads from back to chest. Later cosmonauts used their ejection seats at a height of 23,000 feet, but Gagarin landed in the capsule.

The flight of Freedom 7

After the successful flight of the chimpanzee Ham in a Mercury spacecraft in January 1961, there was pressure to accelerate the man-in-space program. Wisely, the National Aeronautics and Space Administration (NASA), which was responsible for the program, refused to rate prestige higher than the safety of its astronauts.

The Mercury team were, naturally, disappointed when Gagarin completed his orbital flight before they had made even their first manned sub-orbital test; but NASA's caution helped to ensure that all six Mercury spacecraft launched from Cape Canaveral (now Cape Kennedy), and all ten of the two-man Gemini spacecraft which followed, would be recovered safely.

The first American to journey into space was Commander Alan B. Shepard, whose Mercury spacecraft Freedom 7 was launched on a sub-orbital flight down the Atlantic Missile Range, by a modified Redstone rocket, on May 5, 1961. He reached a peak speed of 5,100 m.p.h. during the flight, which took

May 5, 1961: Cdr. Alan Shepard is launched from Cape Canaveral to become the first U.S. astronaut.

him to a height of 115 miles before dropping him gently in the Atlantic, by parachute, still inside his spacecraft, 302 miles from land. The flight lasted just fifteen and a half minutes. A similar ballistic trajectory was followed by Captain Virgil (Gus) I. Grissom in the capsule Liberty Bell 7, on July 21, 1961.

Back on April 25, an attempt had been made to put a Mercury spacecraft into orbit, using an Atlas booster of the kind that would be employed for the manned flights. The rocket failed to enter its planned trajectory and had to be destroyed by the range safety officer forty seconds after take-off. The capsule, containing a 'mechanical astronaut', was separated and recovered safely; but it was clearly necessary to try again before attempting manned orbital flight.

The repeat test was made on September 13, 1961 and proved completely successful. A three orbit flight was made on November 29, this time with a chimpanzee named Enos on board. All was now ready for the most important space-launch that the United States had ever attempted.

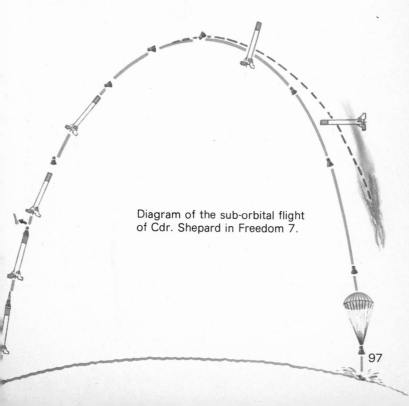

Diagram of the sub-orbital flight of Cdr. Shepard in Freedom 7.

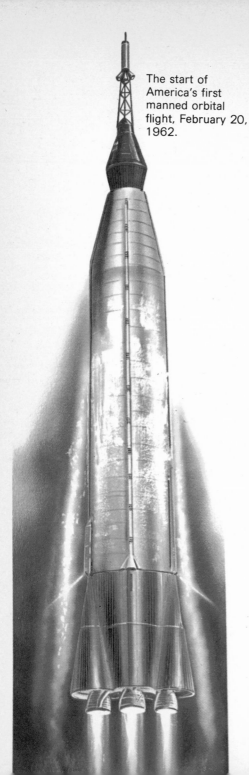

The start of America's first manned orbital flight, February 20, 1962.

The 15,000-mph TV tube

Seven men were chosen, out of hundreds of applicants, as the astronauts for Project Mercury. The requirements were rigid. All the men had to be highly skilled test pilots with college degrees, under forty years of age and less than 5 foot 11 inches tall. A stable family background was essential. Even then, the seven who were chosen had to spend two years in training, to build up their fitness and learn everything possible about the spacecraft, its launch vehicle and the sequence of operations during launch, orbit and recovery.

Two of the seven men made sub-orbital flights; one had to drop out of the program because of bad health; the other four all made successful orbital flights.

Lieutenant Colonel John Glenn of the U.S. Marine Corps became America's first orbiting spaceman. On February 20, 1962, his spacecraft Friendship 7 was lifted off the launch pad by its Atlas booster for an almost perfect three-orbit mission. A slight mishap tended to increase rather than diminish the confidence of the astronauts, for

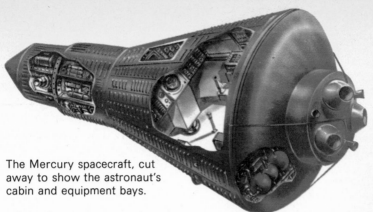

The Mercury spacecraft, cut away to show the astronaut's cabin and equipment bays.

when the automatic control system went wrong prior to re-entry, Glenn took over the firing of the retro-rocket himself and made a completely successful splash-down in the sea, 166 miles east of Grand Turk Island in the Bahamas.

A similar three-orbit flight was made by Lieutenaut Commander Scott Carpenter on May 24, 1962. On October 3, Commander Walter Schirra completed six orbits, and the Mercury program was brought to a triumphant conclusion with a 22-orbit flight by Major Gordon Cooper on May 15–16, 1963. After traveling 583,469 miles, he controlled his re-entry manually and came down a mere four and a half miles from the recovery ship.

The capability of the Atlas booster limited Mercury's weight to about one ton and its diameter to 6 feet 2½ inches. Shaped like a TV cathode-ray tube, it was constructed of inner and outer shells of nickel-alloy, seam-welded together. The blunt curved end face (the heat-shield), against which the astronaut sat, re-entered the atmosphere first and was coated with layers of special plastic which were burned away by friction from the airflow, so keeping down the temperature of the spacecraft itself. This is known as ablative cooling.

At launch, the spacecraft carried on its nose a tower structure containing a rocket to pull it clear of the booster in the event of an emergency during launching. This tower was jettisoned before the spacecraft entered orbit. The retro-rocket panel was mounted in the center of the heat-shield and was jettisoned after burn-out. No ejection seat was fitted, and the astronaut descended inside the spacecraft, under a recovery parachute.

Space twins

As a follow-up to Mercury, NASA decided to put into orbit a series of two-man satellites, under Project Gemini—named after the heavenly twins of the zodiac. The spacecraft were to be slightly enlarged versions of the Mercury capsule, but with ejection seats for the crew instead of a rocket escape tower for emergency use. The launch vehicle was to be based on the Titan II ICBM, and a number of ambitious experiments were to be made. In particular, it was hoped that some astronauts would leave the cabin in orbit, to find out how difficult it would be to work in space, and that one or two flights would include docking of the spacecraft into an orbiting Agena satellite, to prove the ability of spacecraft to rendezvous in orbit.

Before the first Geminis were ready for launch, Russia scored some more notable 'firsts'. On August 6–7, 1961 (before any American had gone into orbit), Gherman Titov made the first day-long orbital journey in Vostok II. On August 11–12, 1962, Russia demonstrated its own, different, ideas on 'space twins' by launching Andrian Nikolayev in Vostok III and Paval Popovich in Vostok IV on successive days and announcing that, before landing on August 15, the two spacecraft had come within three miles of each other in orbit.

This near-rendezvous was repeated in June 1963, with an interesting twist. The Vostok VI spacecraft that approached to within three miles of Valery Bykovsky's Vostok V contained Valentina Tereshkova, first woman to travel in space.

The next spacecraft launched by Russia, on October 12, 1964, was Voskhod I, carrying a three-man crew. Only Colonel Vladimir Komarov was a pilot, Lieutenant Boris Yegorov being an Air Force doctor and Konstantin Feoktistov, a civilian scientist. This first flight of a multi-seat spacecraft is memorable for several reasons. The crew wore only lightweight clothing instead of spacesuits for part of the journey and landed inside Voskhod I, which used aerodynamic braking devices inside the atmosphere and a special type of parachute, and was slowed further by a retro-rocket just above the ground. The only question mark hanging over the achievement was why a flight intended officially 'to carry out extended medico-

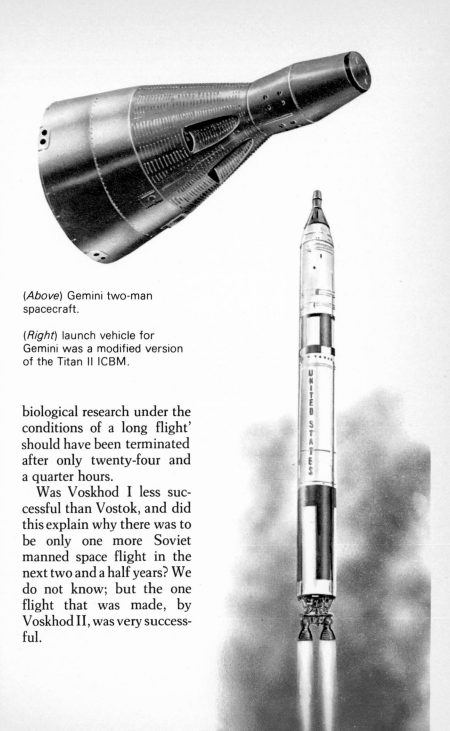

(*Above*) Gemini two-man spacecraft.

(*Right*) launch vehicle for Gemini was a modified version of the Titan II ICBM.

biological research under the conditions of a long flight' should have been terminated after only twenty-four and a quarter hours.

Was Voskhod I less successful than Vostok, and did this explain why there was to be only one more Soviet manned space flight in the next two and a half years? We do not know; but the one flight that was made, by Voskhod II, was very successful.

Walking in space

Voskhod II, launched from the Soviet cosmodrome at Baikonur, east of the Aral Sea, on March 18, 1965, carried a crew of only two: Colonel Pavel Belyayev and Lieutenant Colonel Aleksei Leonov. It differed from its predecessor in one other important aspect, in that an airlock was fitted above the entrance hatch, to enable one of the cosmonauts to leave the spacecraft and 'float' around outside while in orbit without lowering the pressure inside the main cabin.

According to the official Soviet account of the flight, the spacecraft was launched by a new kind of rocket, 150 feet tall and powered by seven engines developing a total of 1,430,000 pounds of thrust. It entered an orbit with a record apogee of 308 miles. During the second orbit, Leonov entered the airlock, in which he remained for ten minutes to check his suit and equipment; then he opened the hatch of the airlock and pushed himself out into space.

Leonov 'walked' in space for ten minutes, linked to Voskhod II by a 16-foot tether. He activated a television camera mounted on the outside of the spacecraft, looked down at the outside of the spacecraft, looked down at the Earth passing hundreds of miles beneath him at 15,000 mph, and even initiated a tumbling motion to see if it would cuase disorientation or vertigo. Afterward, 'with slight difficulty', he re-entered the airlock, which was jettisoned after he returned to the main cabin.

The United States moved quickly to close the gap. Within a few days of Leonov's achievement, on March 23, a Titan rocket put the manned Gemini III spacecraft Molly Brown into orbit. Its pilot, Virgil (Gus) Grissom, was the first man to make more than one flight in a spacecraft. For the first time, also, Grissom and his co-pilot John Young practiced the controlled maneuvering of a spacecraft, using thrust units to change the plane and height of their orbit — an essential preliminary to attempts at orbital rendezvous.

Gemini IV followed on June 3, carrying astronauts James McDivitt and Edward White. On the third orbit, White opened his hatch and left the cabin for twenty minutes, during which time he maneuvered around the craft at the end of a tether, by propelling himself with a compressed-oxygen reaction-unit.

Hand-held maneuvering unit used by U.S. astronauts during space-walks. Three small rocket motors, running on hydrazine and water, each give one or two pounds of thrust.

Rendezvous in space

It had been intended that Gemini IV should rendezvous in orbit with the burned-out second stage of its Titan II launch vehicle, but this plan was abandoned as the stage was in a much lower orbit than expected. Instead, this station-keeping exercise was made one of the primary tasks for Gemini V, which went into space on August 21, 1965, carrying Gordon Cooper and Charles Conrad. Cooper thus became the first astronaut to make two orbital flights.

Gemini V remained in space for more than eight days—a new record—completing 119 orbits in 190 hours 56 minutes. It kept station for a time with the second stage of its booster, so paving the way for what was to be one of the most memorable encounters between human beings in history.

The great adventure began on December 14, 1965, when Frank Borman and James Lovell were blasted off the launch-pad at Cape Kennedy in Gemini VII, at the start of what was to be, among other things, the longest flight yet attempted. They had already been in space for eleven days when Walter Schirra and Thomas Stafford joined them in Gemini VI—'joined them' literally, for at 2:27 p.m. on December 15, Gemini VI matched its speed to that of its sistercraft and the two journeyed around the world together in the first rendezvous between two manned spaceships.

Photographs taken by Stafford provide dramatic proof of what followed as Schirra changed orbit repeatedly, at one stage bringing the nose of his craft to within one foot of the nose of Gemini VII, before breaking formation and flying around his partners in space. For four hours the two crews remained within twenty feet of each other, their lack of relative movement combining with the deathly quiet of space to make it difficult to believe that they were all hurtling around the globe at over 15,000 mph.

Schirra and Stafford landed next day, making the first successful guided re-entry. Borman and Lovell did not return until the 18th, after 205 orbits and a record fourteen days in space. With only half the flights planned for Project Gemini completed, and so much accomplished, NASA had little reason to doubt that all its objectives would be achieved.

Docking and working in space

After the achievement of Gemini VI and VII, the next step was the actual docking of one craft in another in orbit.

On March 16, 1966, the specially modified Agena 8 target satellite was put into orbit, with an adaptor at one end into which astronauts Neil Armstrong and David Scott were to attempt to dock their Gemini VIII spacecraft. When they blasted off in pursuit of the Agena, entered the same orbit, closed in on it and docked successfully, all seemed to be going entirely as planned; but no sooner were the two craft 'locked' together than trouble began.

Without warning, the Gemini began spinning rapidly, giving the impression of being completely out of control. Quickly, the crew disengaged from the Agena and switched to emergency control, which was designed to utilize an on-board computer program to bring the spacecraft down safely in the absence of any normal control. The subsequent land-

ing was not only safe but on target in the Pacific recovery area. Investigation showed that the spin was caused by one of Gemini's maneuvering thrusters having jammed open.

Gemini IX, carrying Thomas Stafford and Eugene Cernan, was also not completely successful, because when it made contact with its target it could not dock. The fairings covering the docking adaptor had not jettisoned. However, Cernan spent over two hours 'walking' in space.

After that, everything went right for Gemini. On July 18, 1966, astronauts John Young and Michael Collins docked Gemini X in the Agena 10 target satellite and used the remaining fuel in the Agena's tanks to take them to a second rendezvous with the Agena 8 used in Gemini VIII's docking experiment. Collins then left the cabin and propelled himself toward Agena 8 with a hand-held maneuvering unit.

Gemini XI, piloted by Charles Conrad and Richard Gordon, docked with Agena 11 on September 12 and used the Agena's engine to climb to a new orbit with a record apogee (for a manned craft) of 850 miles. Gordon spent forty-four minutes

(*Left*) Gemini spacecraft docked in Agena target satellite in orbit. (*Below*) astronaut Michael Collins takes a close look at Agena 8 after Gemini X's second rendezvous.

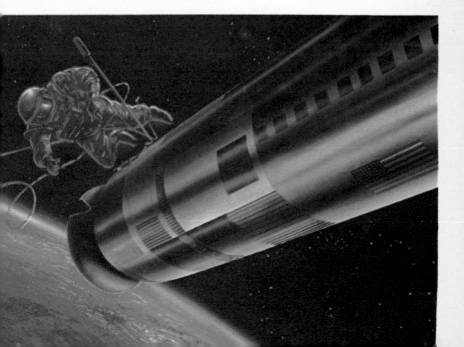

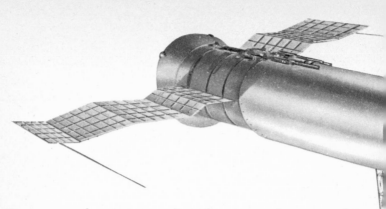

in space, performing a number of pre-set tasks—an exploit that was repeated with even greater success during the flight of Gemini XII, when Edwin Aldrin spent five and a half hours in space. When Aldrin and James Lovell landed safely on November 15, 1966, after fifty-nine orbits, Project Gemini had been completed.

The first automatic docking

Since the day when scientists and enthusiasts began to seriously consider how spacecraft might travel to the Moon, there have been two basic schools of thought on the best way of making the journey.

One method, which the United States decided to use in their Project Apollo, was to go first into Earth orbit, go on from there to the Moon, enter lunar orbit and make the descent to the surface and subsequent ascent in a separate small landing craft.

An alternative technique, which is often said to be favored in the Soviet Union, is to begin by building a space station in orbit around the Earth. The flight to the Moon would then be made from this space station, directly onto the lunar surface, followed by a return to the space station. Given a space station in Earth orbit, this is probably the less complicated and hence safer of the two techniques.

Whether the Russians do, in fact, intend to start their lunar voyages from a space station we cannot yet know, but a most significant event took place twenty minutes after midday (Moscow time) on October 30, 1967.

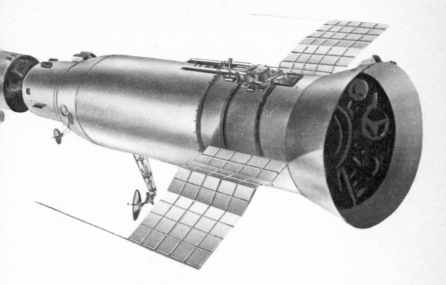

On October 28, 1967, the 186th in Russia's series of Cosmos satellites had been put into an orbit with an apogee of 146 miles and perigee of 130 miles. On the 29th, the orbit of this satellite was adjusted, so that it would pass directly over the spot where Cosmos-188 was waiting on the nose of its launch rocket.

After Cosmos-188 had entered orbit successfully, Cosmos-186 began homing on it, with the aid of what the *Tass* news agency report called 'a beam link-up unit'. Eventually, Cosmos-186 docked into its space partner, completely automatically, and the two continued to orbit as one for eight and a half hours until they were separated by a command signal from the ground.

The entire operation was recorded by television cameras and telemetry equipment on board the satellites. Cosmos-186 was recovered successfully from orbit on October 31.

Some day Russia may assemble entire space stations automatically by this technique, either as huge laboratories in space or as a preliminary to manned flight to the Moon.

REACHING FOR THE MOON

First to the Moon

Less than one year after the first satellite went into orbit around the Earth, both the United States and Russia began their Moon programs. This was not as ambitious as it appeared. A speed of 18,000 mph is needed to put a satellite into orbit; the addition of another 7,000 mph is sufficient to reach the 'escape velocity' needed to overcome the pull of gravity and travel to the Moon.

The Americans tried first on October 11, 1958, with an 85-pound probe known as Pioneer I, launched by a three-stage Thor-Able rocket. After the probe had traveled 70,700 miles, gravity overtook it and it fell back toward the Earth. Russia's 796-pound Luna I got within 4,600 miles of the Moon, before racing on to enter an orbit around the Sun. Pioneer IV followed it into solar orbit.

Then, on September 14, 1959, thirty-four hours after leaving Earth, Luna II crashed down on to the lunar surface, at 5,400 mph, scattering tiny emblems bearing the 'hammer and sickle' badge. It was a tremendous achievement—the first time man had made physical contact with another body in space—but there was greater to come.

Less than a month later, on October 4, Luna III passed round the Moon, taking photographs of the surface from a height of 40,000 miles as it did so. Transmitted to Earth by television, these photographs gave us our first exciting glimpse of the side of the Moon which is always hidden from our view.

Luna III, which sent back the first photographs of the Moon's hidden face.

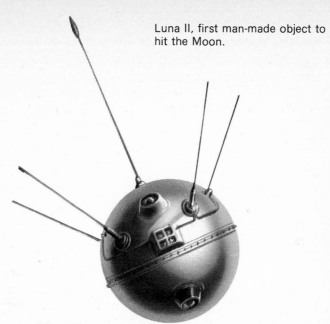

Luna II, first man-made object to hit the Moon.

Close-up of the Moon

The photographs sent back by Luna III whetted the scientists' appetite for more. There was so much they wanted to know about Earth's nearest neighbor in space, such as what it is made of and whether the surface is hard enough to support the weight of a spacecraft.

America tackled the problem by building a series of Ranger spacecraft which were intended to take television pictures of the lunar surface and study the composition of the soil as they approached the Moon, then eject an instrument package which would be slowed sufficiently by retro-rocket to make a reasonably soft landing. This was too much to expect from any automatic spacecraft in 1961–62, and all of the first five Rangers failed for various reasons.

After that the mission was simplified, so that Ranger had only to take photographs as it crashed down on to the lunar surface. Ranger 7, launched on July 28, 1964, sent back 4,316 photographs, some showing craters only a few feet in diameter. The photographs were hundreds of times better than the finest results achieved through a telescope on Earth. Ranger 8 did equally well; so NASA decided to allow pictures transmitted

111

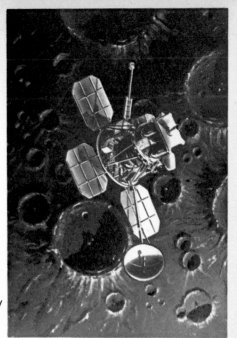

(*Opposite page*) Ranger spacecraft, which sent back the first close-up photographs of the surface of the Moon.

(*Right*) America's five Lunar Orbiter spacecraft photographed more than 99 percent of the surface of the Moon—a total of about 14 million square miles—from low orbit. One of the primary objectives was to survey potential landing sites for Apollo manned flights to the Moon.

by Ranger 9 to be shown live on the public television circuits. Millions of viewers were thus able to get a close-up view of the Moon's surface through the eyes of the spacecraft's cameras as it hurtled down in the last minutes of its journey.

Ranger was followed by Lunar Orbiter, which was intended to go into orbit around the Moon and photograph the surface from a height of less than thirty miles. It was hoped that the resulting photographs would enable experts to choose the best possible landing sites for Apollo manned spacecraft.

Five Lunar Orbiters were launched between August 10, 1966 and August 2, 1967. They provided the best close-up photographs of immense areas of the Moon's surface, located the required Apollo landing sites and produced the first detailed scientific knowledge of the lunar gravitational field, topography and geology. In doing so, they sent back photographs of the bare mountains and craters of the Moon so vivid that only an astronaut, trained in what to expect and eager to go there, could look at them without feeling a shiver of fear.

First landings on the Moon

Good as were the photographs taken by Ranger, they were no substitute for the information that could be gained by a spacecraft sitting on the surface of the Moon. So, simultaneously with Lunar Orbiter, the United States developed a strange three-legged robot explorer known as Surveyor for the difficult task of attempting a gentle landing on the Moon.

This time, United States scientists knew from the start that they had little chance of being first, as Russia had sent five Luna probes to the Moon between April 2, 1963 and December 3, 1965, almost certainly in unsuccessful attempts at a landing.

It was no surprise, therefore, when Luna IX achieved the first 'soft' landing on the Moon on February 3, 1966 and began transmitting the first pictures from the surface. The desolate scene they revealed was described by one commentator as a cross between a slag heap and a lump of pumice-stone.

The main Luna IX spacecraft, weighing 3,269 pounds, carried equipment to correct its course en route to the Moon and orientation devices to ensure that it would be vertical to the lunar surface when its retro-rocket fired at a height of about 46 miles. The spherical payload package was ejected just before touch-down. Four petal-like covers protecting the television camera then opened in such a way that they placed the package in an upright position; aerials extended automatically and the camera began its work.

Nearly four months later, on May 30, Surveyor I was launched by an Atlas-Centaur rocket from Cape Kennedy. It soft-landed successfully on June 2 and sent back more than ten thousand high-quality photographs during the next two weeks. Once again, although not first, America reaped better scientific results from its more advanced equipment.

Surveyors II and IV crashed on the Moon; but Surveyors III, V, VI and VII continued the good work of Surveyor I, not only taking photographs but also using a mechanical scoop to examine the surface of the Moon and a radioactive device to determine the constituents of the soil. Surveyor VI also made history when its rocket engines were restarted by a signal from Earth, causing it to rise ten feet and move sideways eight feet to a new position—providing valuable data on take-off from the Moon for the Apollo program.

114

First spacecraft to make a soft
landing on the Moon and send
back to Earth photographs taken
on the lunar surface was the
Russian Luna IX. Its payload
package (*right*) was ejected from
the main spacecraft just before
touch-down. Even better
photographs were transmitted
by America's Surveyor spacecraft, one of which is depicted
above firing its retro-rocket.

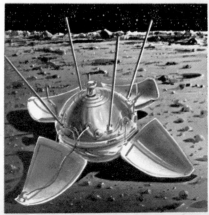

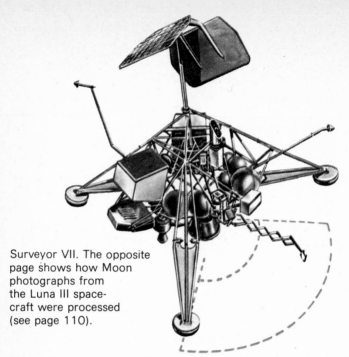

Surveyor VII. The opposite page shows how Moon photographs from the Luna III spacecraft were processed (see page 110).

Portrait of a spacecraft

The main framework of the Surveyor VII spacecraft was a triangular structure of thin-wall aluminium tubing, which provided mounting surfaces and attachment points for the landing gear, retro-rocket engine, vernier engines and associated fuel tanks, thermal components, antennae and other electronic and mechanical assemblies.

A mast in the center of the main triangular structure supported the high-gain directional antenna, which transmitted 600-line television data, and a 30 × 44 inch panel carrying 3,960 solar cells which converted the sun's energy into usable electric voltage to power all the spacecraft's equipment. Two low-gain antennae received ground commands and transmitted other data including 200-line television.

Surveyor stood about ten feet high and, with its tripod landing gear extended, could be placed within a fourteen-foot circle. A landing leg was hinged to each of the three lower corners of the main frame and an aluminium honeycomb footpad was attached to the outer end of each leg. Touchdown

116

shock on landing was absorbed by the footpads and by aircraft-type hydraulic shock absorbers.

Three thermal compartments housed sensitive electronic equipment which had to be protected from extremes of heat or cold. A spherical solid-propellent retro-rocket was fitted within the center cavity of the main frame and was used to slow the spacecraft from an approach velocity of about 6,000 mph to approximately 350 mph as it neared the lunar surface. It developed from 8,000 to 10,000 pounds of thrust for about thirty-nine seconds. Three small vernier chambers provided thrust during the mid-course correction and final descent phases of the flight.

Scientific equipment carried by Surveyor included a survey television camera which could be focused from four feet to infinity by command signal from Earth; a total of eleven mirrors to enable the television camera to photograph parts of the spacecraft, the lunar soil and the soil sampler; a device to determine whether magnetic particles are present in the surface soil; and a radioactive device for determining the chemical properties of the soil. The complete spacecraft weighed 2,288 pounds.

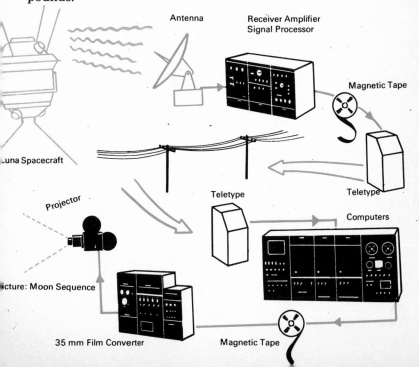

Antenna

Receiver Amplifier
Signal Processor

Magnetic Tape

Luna Spacecraft

Projector

Teletype

Teletype

Computers

Picture: Moon Sequence

35 mm Film Converter

Magnetic Tape

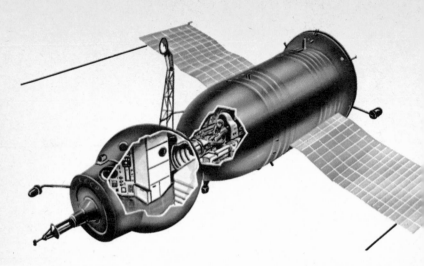

The first space laboratory. The first man to die during a space flight, on April 24, 1967, was Cosmonaut Vladimir Komarov. After 18 orbits in the new Soyuz I spacecraft, he made a successful re-entry but was killed when the craft's landing parachute became twisted. The second manned test of the Soyuz was made in October 1968, when Cosmonaut Georgy Beregovoi, in Soyuz 3, effected a successful rendezvous with the unmanned Soyuz 2. Then, on January 16, 1969, came a major success when Soyuz 4, piloted by Vladimir Shatalov, was docked by manual control in Soyuz 5, containing Cosmonauts Boris Volynov, Alexei Yeliseyev and Yevgeny Khrunov. Yeliseyev and Khrunov subsequently donned spacesuits and transferred to Soyuz 4, in which they eventually returned to Earth.

As can be seen in the picture above the Soyuz spacecraft consists of a spherical laboratory/rest compartment on the nose of the re-entry capsule, which is itself attached to an equipment section with two large solar cell panels.

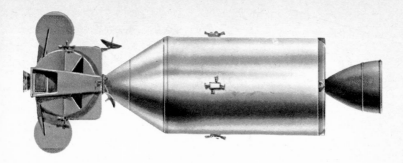

(*Above*) the three-part Apollo spacecraft, made up of (*left to right*)
the lunar module, command module, and service module.
(*Opposite page, below*) Apollo service module, housing fuel, electrical
power supplies and propulsion unit.

The Apollo Moon-ship

Illustrations on this and the following ten pages depict the
greatest adventure ever undertaken by man—the journey to,
and exploration of, the Moon. Of necessity, they concentrate
on the United States' Project Apollo, as the Russians have released no details of their man-on-the-Moon program.

The Apollo spacecraft is made up of three major components, consisting of a command module housing the three-man
crew; a service module housing fuel, electrical power supplies
and propulsion unit; and the lunar module in which the actual
landing is made on the Moon.

The conical command module is 10½ feet high and weighs
5 tons. It consists of an inner pressurized compartment of aluminium honeycomb and an outer shell of stainless steel honeycomb, with a plastic ablative heat shield covering the entire
outer surface. On its nose it carries an escape rocket tower of the
kind used in the Mercury program.

The largest component is the service module, which is constructed of aluminium and is 23 feet high, with a weight of 24
tons. The engine fitted to this component uses storable liquid
propellents and develops a 22,000-pound thrust.

Looking like a huge spider, the lunar module is designed to
carry two crew-men. It is 23 feet tall and weighs 14 tons. Separate liquid-propellent rocket engines are fitted for descent to
and ascent from the Moon.

Everything is giant-size

Everything about the Apollo program is giant-size. The Saturn V rocket that is used to put the three-component spacecraft on course for the Moon is so enormous that it would be almost impossible to transport even its second stage by normal means from where it is built to where the complete rocket is assembled; so a special barge had to be built to carry it by water.

The third stage of the rocket goes by air from the manufacturing plant in Los Angeles to Cape Kennedy; but the only aircraft large enough to carry it is the Super Guppy, an incredible

cargo-plane with the largest freight-hold of any commercial air transport.

Assembly of the complete Saturn V vehicle is done in the Vertical Assembly Building (VAB), a metal-walled steelframe skyscraper, 552 feet high, which is the largest building in the world. The fully assembled Saturn V and its servicing tower are then taken three and a half miles to the launch-pad on a 2,450-ton crawler-transporter. The largest land machine ever built, the crawler-transporter moves on four twin-track 'bogies' and has a control cab at each end.

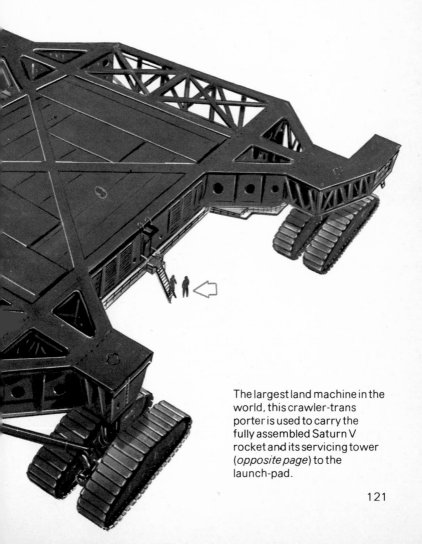

The largest land machine in the world, this crawler-transporter is used to carry the fully assembled Saturn V rocket and its servicing tower (*opposite page*) to the launch-pad.

121

America's mightiest space vehicle

Back in the mid-1950's, America almost abandoned development of the Atlas ICBM when calculations showed that a weapon of the required performance would weigh 200 tons and need seven rocket engines, each of 125,000-pound thrust, for the first stage alone. Only when United States scientists produced a lightweight thermonuclear warhead, which enabled Atlas to be trimmed to 115 tons and three engines, did the program get underway.

Today even the 'impracticable' 200-ton ICBM would

look small by comparison with the mighty family of Saturn space vehicles built under America's man-on-the-Moon program. The smallest of the family was Saturn I, a two-stage rocket standing 190 feet tall and with a launching weight of 520 tons. All ten launches, made from 1961 to 1965, were successful, two of them being used to put dummy Apollo spacecraft into Earth orbit.

Uprated Saturn I differs mainly in having engines of higher thrust, enabling it to put payloads of up to twenty tons into orbit around the Earth. First launched on February 26, 1966, its main task was to put the first man-carrying Apollo into Earth orbit as a preliminary to the actual flights to the Moon.

Saturn V, the Moon rocket, is so enormous that the second stage of the Uprated Saturn I is used as its payload-carrying third stage. With the Apollo spacecraft in position on its nose, it stands 353 feet 5 inches high—about 50 feet taller than the Statue of Liberty—and weighs an incredible 2,725 tons at lift-off. The five first-stage engines give a total of 7½ million pounds of thrust.

(*Opposite page, left to right*) the huge size of Saturn V is underlined by these drawings, which show the Vostok and Mercury/Atlas launch vehicles to the same scale.

(*Below*) Saturn I rocket used for early flight trials of the Apollo spacecraft.

Saturn V in action

The date is July 16, 1969; the place Cape Kennedy, Florida. The very earth trembles under the blast of Saturn V's engines as they lift the great rocket off its launch-pad. Burning fifteen tons of kerosene and liquid oxygen every second, they take the rocket to a height of about forty-one miles and a speed of 6,000 mph in two and a half minutes. Then, its 560,600 gallons of propellents consumed, the first stage falls away.

Only by using a more potent liquid oxygen and liquid hydrogen propellent mix, can the remaining stages provide the needed escape velocity. The second stage, with five engines, boosts the spacecraft to near orbital speed at a height of about 115 miles in six and a half minutes of operation, burning more than one ton of propellents every second as it does so.

The complete Saturn V rocket stands about 50 feet higher than the Statue of Liberty. The pictures on the opposite page show (*top*) the third stage, which puts the spacecraft into Earth orbit and then injects it into its lunar trajectory, and (*bottom*) the Apollo service and command modules.

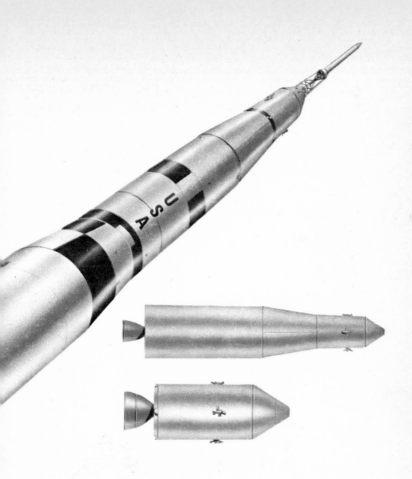

After the second stage has dropped away, the third stage ignites and burns for about 2½ minutes to put itself and the spacecraft into a parking orbit around the Earth. Then, when everything has been checked and rechecked, and the astronauts are ready, the third stage re-ignites for six minutes, leaving orbit and accelerating to 24,200 mph. Its motors silent, it then falls away, leaving Apollo and its crew to speed on alone into the dark emptiness of space. The greatest voyage of discovery has begun.

The Apollo spacecraft prior to lunar landing attempt, with the lunar module now transferred to the nose of the command module.

Landing on the Moon

For the astronauts packed inside the small Apollo command module, the difficult part of the operation begins when the third stage of the Saturn V booster falls away behind them. Before this happened, the astronauts had to transfer the lunar landing module from the third stage to the nose of the spacecraft.

They now start to follow silently their 73-hour free-fall trajectory of nearly a quarter of a million miles. Their course and speed are checked constantly by the ground crew at Cape Kennedy. Mid-course corrections of trajectory and speed can be made by using the storable liquid-propellent engine built in the service module.

Earth's gravity never gives up its struggle to pull them back, and every second their speed falls a little lower. Then, after what seems a long, long time, the spacecraft begins to accelerate again. The Moon's gravity now has them in its hold, carrying them toward the dimly lit, pock-marked surface that gets nearer and nearer. But all is well, and they are soon in orbit again—this time around the Moon.

As they circle about seventy miles above the lunar surface, the spacecraft's inclination to the Moon's axis, and the height and inclination of its orbit are worked out precisely.

Two of the astronauts transfer to the landing craft from the command module, detach it and fire its rocket engine to put it into a new, eccentric orbit which descends to within about 60,000 feet of the landing site. After leaving this orbit, the landing craft is able to hover for up to two minutes, 100 feet above the ground, while the men decide whether or not a safe landing can be made. It would be bitterly disappointing if, having got so far, they had to turn back. Even worse would be to make a bad landing and be unable to take off again.

This time, all looks perfect; the rocket engine is throttled back and the lunar module sinks gently down on the lunar surface. The man on the Moon is no longer a fable.

Lunar module firing its retro-rocket for a soft touch-down on the surface of the Moon.

Take-off from the Moon.

Man on the Moon

It is now the early morning of July 21, 1969. Clambering down the ladder from the lunar module, Neil Armstrong plants his left foot firmly on the surface of the Moon. Soon he is joined by Edwin Aldrin, and the two astronauts begin their task of photographing and collecting samples of rock.

This completed, the astronauts face one of the most difficult and hazardous parts of the entire mission — rejoining Michael Collins in orbit. They have to act as their own launch-crew, with nobody to check out their craft and perform the launch operation for them.

Only the cabin portion of the craft is to perform the rendezvous. The base, carrying the landing legs, forms a launch-pad and will be left behind on the Moon.

128

Satisfied that conditions are as good as they could possibly be for the start of their long return journey, the astronauts ignite the landing craft's rocket engine and, with a final look around at the view never before seen by human eyes, they lift off—up into orbit and to a reunion with the third astronaut. After transferring back into the command module, they cast adrift the landing craft cabin, which is to be left in Moon orbit.

More very precise calculations, in space and on Earth, tell the astronauts when to start the engine of the service module to blast them out of orbit and into a trajectory toward the Earth. Again, mid-course corrections can be made and, shortly before entering the upper fringes of the atmosphere, the service module is also jettisoned. It would have added too much weight to fit retro-rockets; so the command module has to re-enter the atmosphere at 25,000 mph, its heat-shield glowing white-hot as it burns away. The aerodynamic shape of the capsule provides a limited amount of glide path control at this critical stage.

Finally, the recovery parachutes open and the astronauts breathe a great sigh of relief as they drift slowly down on the last few miles of their journey. The Earth never looked more beautiful.

In November 1969, the United States launched its second successful landing on the Moon, Apollo 12. These two flights were the first of several Apollo missions for the purpose of lunar exploration.

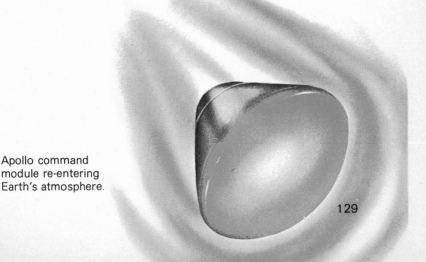

Apollo command
module re-entering
Earth's atmosphere.

129

Space station in orbit

The usefulness of space stations is not doubted. Even small ones have obvious military value for reconnaissance and 'spy' missions. Large ones offer an immense number of attractions as staging posts for flights to the Moon and planets, and for scientific experiments that cannot be performed on Earth.

Space station astronomers would benefit from being able to work without the hindrance of clouds and from being above the atmosphere which distorts everything studied through telescopes on Earth. Physicists could investigate a whole new spectrum of phenomena under the weightless conditions in orbit; while doctors could study the treatment of those with heart diseases, in conditions where their systems would be spared the effort of working against gravity.

No one is likely to find the money for big space stations until their practicability has been proved with small ones. That was the intention of the U.S. Air Force's MOL (Manned Orbiting Laboratory) program.

To get a worthwhile space station into orbit quickly, at minimum cost, the USAF planned to utilize existing hardware to a large extent. The obvious way of getting astronauts back after a spell in space was to use a well-proven Gemini two-man spacecraft. So the men were intended to travel into space and back in Gemini B, differing only in detail from the capsule already employed in ten highly successful missions. Launch vehicle for the MOL mission was to be Tital IIIM, a standard U.S. rocket based on a Titan core, with a pair of huge solid-propellent boosters strapped to the sides. The laboratory between the Titan core and the Gemini capsule was to be a cylinder of the same diameter as the launcher, fitted out with minimal living, working and sleeping accommodations and carrying a number of experiments to be performed by the astronauts during their stay in orbit. The only concession to comfort was an air-conditioning and pressurization system, permitting the men to take off their spacesuits.

Like many modern military projects, the MOL program was abandoned in 1969 for financial reasons, but it pointed the way for others to follow.

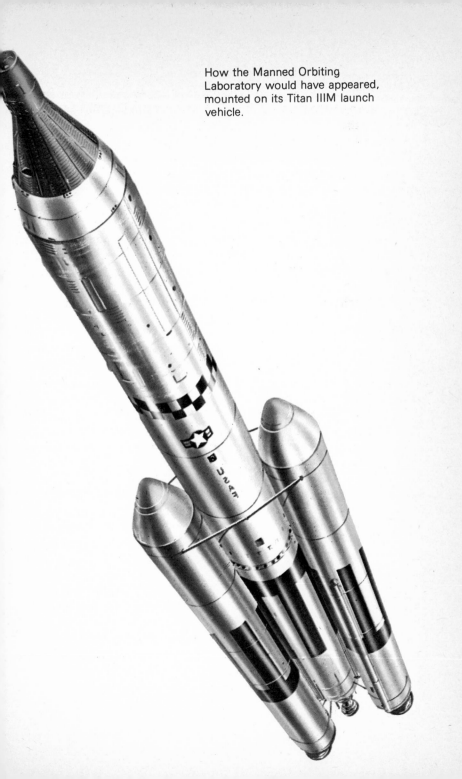

How the Manned Orbiting Laboratory would have appeared, mounted on its Titan IIIM launch vehicle.

The giant orbiting workshop that
NASA hopes to put into
orbit in the early 1970's
under its Apollo Applications Program. The module with four
solar cell panels, shown beyond
the Apollo spacecraft, is a solar
telescope built largely from parts
of the Apollo lunar module.

Offshoots of Apollo

Under its Apollo Applications Program (AAP), NASA is now
building a series of orbital workshops. Two Uprated Saturn
launch vehicles are needed for each AAP workshop mission.
The first will orbit a standard Apollo spacecraft (minus the
lunar module) and a three-man crew. Four or five days later the
other Saturn will be launched and will put its own second stage
into orbit about three hundred miles above the Earth.

Spacecraft and second stage will rendezvous and dock in
orbit, and the astronauts will then transfer to the empty stage,
entering the liquid hydrogen tank through the airlock after
checking that no propellent remains inside. They will spend

several days preparing the interior as living quarters and work-shops, by installing partitions and hand holds. It is intended that the astronauts shall spend about one month in the work-shop on the first flight, before returning to Earth in their Apollo command module. About six months later, two more Uprated Saturns will send up a new crew and a large solar telescope re-spectively, enabling the existing workshop to be converted into an orbiting solar observatory.

EXPERIMENTS FOR THE FUTURE

Airplanes without wings

Pilots at Edwards Air Force Base, America's vast flight test center in the Californian desert, call them 'flying stones'. Officially they are lifting-body research aircraft. In everyday terms they are airplanes without wings. To astronauts they seem to offer the most attractive means of getting to and from space stations of the future.

The Apollo astronauts are able to steer their command module to a limited degree as it re-enters the atmosphere on return from the Moon; but what all spacemen dream of having one day is a re-entry vehicle in which they will be able to return safely from outer space and then land, as if in a conventional airplane, at an airport on Earth.

It will be a long time before anyone can give them exactly what they want, but a start has been made with a series of remarkable wingless airplanes that are currently under test at Edwards AFB.

The aircraft come in various shapes, the only common factor being a triangular, or delta, plan-form. The one known as the M2-F2 has a flat top and curved under-surface, with a pair of fins and rudders at the rear. The HL-10 reverses the pattern, with a curved top and flat bottom, plus a triple-finned tail. Both rely on the airfoil shape of their body to provide the lift that is normally obtained from wings.

Despite its alarming appearance, the M2-F2 proved remarkably successful. On fourteen occasions in 1966 it was carried to a height of around 45,000 feet under the wing of a B-52 mother-plane and there released for an unpowered flight.

(*Left*) unmanned X-23A Prime
models were used for re-entry
flight tests at over 17,500 mph.
(*Above top*) design study for future
space ferry.
(*Above*) HL-10 lifting-body
research aircraft.

Rate of descent was fairly rapid, as one would expect from such
a craft; but by diving at 350 mph and then flaring out at low
altitude, the pilot was able to reduce speed to about 190 mph
at touchdown, which occurred about four minutes after
launch.

Unfortunately, before it could be tested in powered form,
the M2-F2 was severely damaged; and the HL-10 proved less
successful on its first flight, requiring some redesign. However,
these pioneer lifting-body aircraft have already been followed
by two more—the jet-powered SV-5J and the rocket-engined
X-24A.

Space ferry re-entering Earth's atmosphere.

Space-taxis

In 1960, the U.S. Air Force awarded contracts to six American companies whose design teams were asked to put on paper their ideas for a series of space vehicles likely to be needed in the future. The project was known as SLOMAR, an abbreviation of Space Logistics, Maintenance and Rescue. The types of craft covered by the contracts included a space-taxi to ferry men and supplies to and from a space station, another to perform assembly work in orbit and a third to rescue astronauts from disabled spacecraft.

The resulting design studies went far beyond the simple outline shapes of such vehicles. Teams of experts investigated the forms of navigational equipment that would be best suited to the spacecraft; techniques of transferring men and freight from one craft to another, or between the spacecraft and an orbiting space station; the clothing that would be needed by the crew and passengers; emergency escape methods for use during launch and re-entry; and even the possibility of using nuclear power plants in the upper stages of the launch vehicles.

Most of the space-taxi designs incorporated a wing-plan of

extreme deltoid form, since it is known that this shape offers a minimum frontal area and so reduces the heat-shield problem. Further research has since defined the optimum shape as being similar to that of the lifting-body vehicles illustrated on pages 134 to 136.

An interesting application of such a shape is the projected Mustard (Multi-Unit Space Transport and Recovery Device) illustrated on this page. Studied by the Preston Division of British Aircraft Corporation, it consists of three winged and piloted craft of similar configuration which are launched vertically as a single three-component 'stack'. The outer units serve as boosters, which break away after launch, leaving the central unit to carry on into orbit to ferry men and materials to space stations. All three units are powered by liquid oxygen/liquid hydrogen rocket engines and are intended to land at conventional airfields at the end of their mission. Thus, the central unit has heat-shield protection for re-entry.

Mustard could carry a 2,500-pound payload, enabling it to cope with the day-to-day requirements of those who will spend much of their working life in 18,000-mph weightlessness hundreds of miles above the Earth.

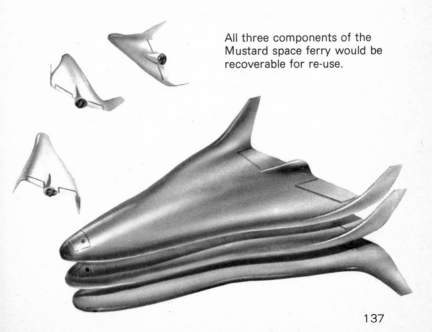

All three components of the Mustard space ferry would be recoverable for re-use.

Survival in space

One of the most difficult tasks connected with space travel is to design an efficient spacesuit. In an utterly hostile and unnatural environment for its wearer, with no air to breathe and no atmospheric pressure, the suit must remedy both deficiencies. It must be able to supply the astronaut with oxygen and exert sufficient pressure around his body to help him collapse his lungs when breathing out and to prevent his blood from boiling.

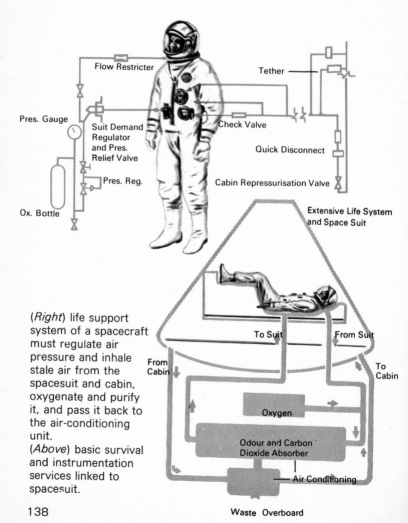

Flow Restricter

Tether

Pres. Gauge

Suit Demand Regulator and Pres. Relief Valve

Check Valve

Quick Disconnect

Pres. Reg.

Cabin Repressurisation Valve

Ox. Bottle

Extensive Life System and Space Suit

(*Right*) life support system of a spacecraft must regulate air pressure and inhale stale air from the spacesuit and cabin, oxygenate and purify it, and pass it back to the air-conditioning unit.
(*Above*) basic survival and instrumentation services linked to spacesuit.

To Suit

From Suit

From Cabin

To Cabin

Oxygen

Odour and Carbon Dioxide Absorber

Air Conditioning

Waste Overboard

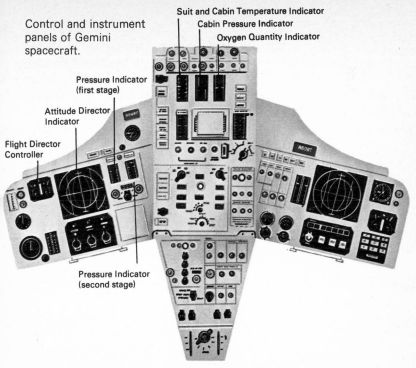

Control and instrument panels of Gemini spacecraft.

Suit and Cabin Temperature Indicator
Cabin Pressure Indicator
Oxygen Quantity Indicator
Pressure Indicator (first stage)
Attitude Director Indicator
Flight Director Controller
Pressure Indicator (second stage)

The suit need not be pressurized permanently if the wearer is traveling inside a pressure-cabin, but it must react instantly to any loss of cabin pressure. Once inflated, it must remain flexible enough for the astronaut to move and work freely. It must be sufficiently tough not to tear when in contact with jagged rocks or pieces of metal. It must make provision for feeding, drinking and disposal of waste products under weightless conditions, without loss of pressure. It must reflect heat and radiation, and it must be as fireproof as possible in any emergency.

Little wonder that hundreds of thousands of dollars have been spent on perfecting suits such as those worn by America's Apollo astronauts. Made by International Latex Corporation, it has no fewer than fifteen layers, some separated by fiberglas. Underneath such suits, astronauts usually wear special long underclothing, embodying tubes through which air or water is passed to keep them cool. Their helmet is an advanced version of a fighter pilot's 'Bone-dome'.

Lunar scooters

It is a pity that the Moon has no atmosphere. If it had, it would be a wonderful place for traveling by hovercraft, being devoid of buildings, trees and wide oceans. The only alternative, of course, is a rocket-motor, if astronauts are to travel over the lunar surface rather than on it.

All kinds of one-man and two-man vehicles have been designed as lunar runabouts. The simplest is a version of Bell Aerosystems' rocket-belt, which is strapped to the astronaut's body and enables him to hop around easily, over fairly large rocks and hills. A device of this kind would be adequate for brief excursions to explore the terrain in the immediate vicinity of a landing site. For more extended trips, astronauts will need a lunar version of a lightweight scooter.

To keep down the weight of equipment that must be deposited on the lunar surface, the first runabouts might be sim-

Bell Aerosystems' rocket-belt has been evolved initially to carry U.S. Army personnel over small obstacles such as rivers, but it could be developed into a mobility system for lunar exploration.

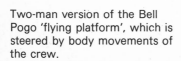

Two-man version of the Bell Pogo 'flying platform', which is steered by body movements of the crew.

ple one-man 'flying platforms', lifted and propelled by a hydrazine rocket motor running on surplus propellent from the lunar landing craft. It would be steered and stabilized by body movements of the astronaut—a natural form of control for anyone accustomed to leaning over when turning a corner on a motorcycle, although its speed of up to 300 mph might seem rather hair-raising at first.

For exploration beyond a fifty-mile radius, Bell has designed a four-legged lunar flying vehicle (LFV), with two open seats mounted side by side over the propulsion unit. Five 100-pound thrust rocket engines would provide lift and propulsion, and six attitude control rockets, of the kind fitted to existing spacecraft, would be used to steer the 400-pound craft. Folded for stowage in a spacecraft, an LFV of the type illustrated below would occupy a space little larger than an average office desk.

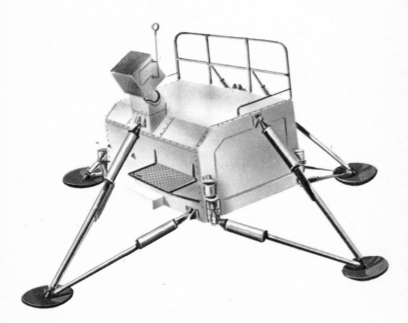

A full-scale mock-up of this two-seat lunar flying vehicle (LFV) has been built by Bell Aerosystems. Such a craft could be delivered to the Moon by an Apollo lunar module and used by astronauts to explore areas beyond a 50-mile radius of their base.

Molabs

Lunar scooters will be ideal for local sightseeing and commuting between bases on the Moon, but larger and more fully equipped craft will be essential for serious exploration of the surface. Such vehicles are known as Molabs (mobile laboratories). To conserve fuel, they will travel on, rather than over, the surface. This has led to the design of several ingenious types of wheels and suspension systems, to cope with the uneven and possibly soft terrain. Boeing's idea of a Molab, for example, has wheels five feet in diameter, with a spring steel carcass and stainless steel mesh for tread. Its unique six-wheel articulated drive would enable the full-size vehicle to scale a seven-foot vertical rock-face and cross crevasses eight feet wide.

The Grumman company's lunar wheel has curved metal 'spokes', designed to flex in such a way that three times as much of the flat tread is on the ground as in the case of a normal wheel. Such designs seem to be more efficient than alternatives such as tracks, rolling balls and 'walking' legs.

The Boeing Molab has been described as looking like 'a twelve-hour cold capsule towing two aspirins'. Devised in

Designed by Boeing and General Motors, this Molab could carry two astronauts on a 14-day, 250-mile expedition over the lunar surface.

collaboration with General Motors, it uses GM's 'locomotive concept'. The cylindrical front end contains a pressurized cabin in which the explorers could work in 'shirtsleeves', protected from heat, cold, airlessness, radiation and meteroid bombardment. As in the Apollo lunar module, the occupants would be suspended from the ceiling in webbed harness.

The 'trailer' is in fact self-propelled, all six wheels of the Molab being driven individually by electric motors powered by a liquid oxygen/liquid hydrogen fuel cell of the kind developed for the Apollo. In an emergency, the trailer could push the whole Molab home. Its main purpose is to carry the fuel, the oxygen for breathing, a drill to collect geological samples from as much as a hundred feet beneath the Moon's surface, and an LFV 'life-boat'.

Molabs are designed to be landed on the Moon, as cargo, by an unmanned Apollo lunar module. They could be controlled from Earth by a television guidance system if operated as robot explorers. Their top speed would be 10 mph, with a normal cruising speed of 5 mph, and they would carry sufficient fuel, food and oxygen for 14-day, 250-mile manned voyages from a landing site.

This Molab design, by the Bendix company, has four flexible metal wheels to provide stability without risk of excessive 'bouncing' in the low gravity.

The first Moon base

Photographs sent back to Earth by Surveyor spacecraft that soft-landed on the Moon conveyed one very positive warning to future astronaut explorers—'Beware micrometeoroids'.

It has always been realized that micrometeoroids must rain down on to the lunar surface, as there is no atmosphere to cause them to burn up like an Earthly shooting star. The possibility of a well-protected astronaut being injured by such a tiny particle is small, but the danger certainly exists. When a Surveyor 1 surprised everyone by transmitting a second series of pictures, after a two-week shut-down during the cold lunar night, the pictures clearly showed micrometeoroid damage to Surveyor's solar cell panel.

For this reason, it will be a primary aim of both the United States and Russia to establish some form of permanent base on

the Moon as soon as possible, to provide a place in which astronauts will be able to live and sleep soundly without fear of bombardment from space.

One day, lunar bases may be almost as elaborate and comfortable as laboratories on Earth, but the first one will probably be very much like America's Manned Orbiting Laboratory (MOL). Even today it would be comparatively easy to land an empty S-IVB Saturn V upper stage on the lunar surface, using a retro-rocket system of the kind perfected for the Surveyor. Once there, it could be pushed over on to its side and covered with lunar soil to provide a solid protection against micrometeoroids.

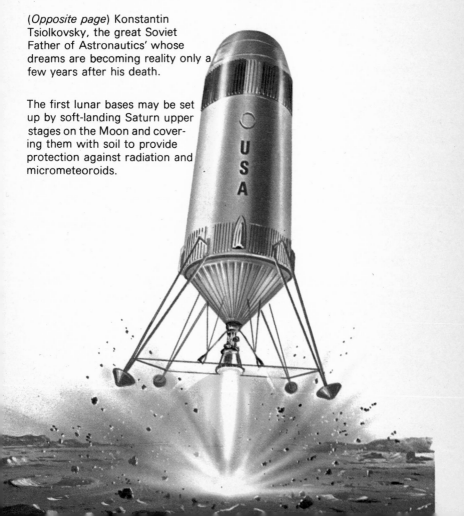

(*Opposite page*) Konstantin Tsiolkovsky, the great Soviet Father of Astronautics' whose dreams are becoming reality only a few years after his death.

The first lunar bases may be set up by soft-landing Saturn upper stages on the Moon and covering them with soil to provide protection against radiation and micrometeoroids.

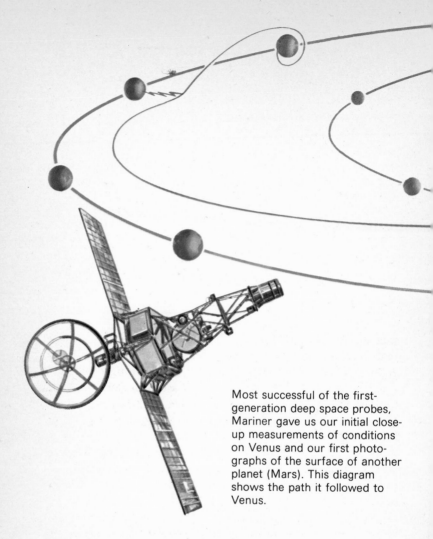

Most successful of the first-generation deep space probes, Mariner gave us our initial close-up measurements of conditions on Venus and our first photographs of the surface of another planet (Mars). This diagram shows the path it followed to Venus.

Pathway to the planets

The Moon is a natural satellite of the Earth, a mere three-day journey from Cape Kennedy or Baikonur. Our next nearest neighbors in space are Earth's eight sisters, the other planets of our solar system. The nearest of them is three months away by a spacecraft of the 1960's, the farthest ones so remote that we know little about them beyond their distance from us and the lengths of their day or night.

Yet already, we have reached out from Earth and made con-

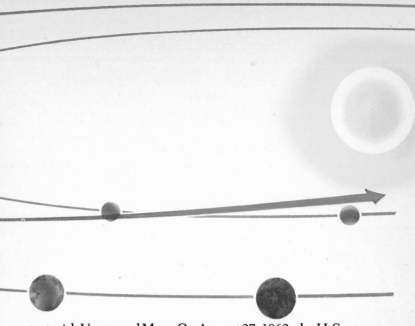

tact with Venus and Mars. On August 27, 1962, the U.S. space-craft Mariner 2 was launched on course for Venus by an Atlas-Agena rocket. For 109 days it raced silently through space in a great sweep around the sun, before passing so close to Venus that the planet's gravity changed its orbit. The data it sent back to Earth ended the hopes of those who thought we might find forms of life of the kind we know on Earth.

Venus, it seemed, was hot, with temperatures as high as 400° C on the surface that is permanently shrouded from our eyes by a blanket of clouds many miles thick. This appeared to leave Mars as the only place in our solar system where we might find recognizable forms of life. Mariner 3, launched on November 5, 1964, failed to shed the fairings covering its solar panels and sent back no data. Mariner 4 followed on November 28. After a 228-day journey of 325 million miles, it was guided to within 5,700 miles of the Martian surface, from where it sent back data and photographs.

The eighty-seven-year-old dream of canals, built by a race of intelligent beings, seemed to fade in a flash. Whatever most people had expected, this was not it. Mars presented in close-up a barren pock-marked face that could just as well have been a corner of the Moon.

147

Mariner 4, Venus 3

The spacecraft that we build as robot explorers of outer space are very different from the sleek streamlined rockets of pre-war science fiction. Streamlining is unnecessary in the emptiness of space, where objects can easily be started on journeys that will never end. Delicate spider-web antennae can be extended with little fear of damage; solar cell panels can be opened out like wings or the sails of a windmill.

Typical of these strange craft of the space age is Mariner 4. Weighing 575 pounds, it was equipped not only with instruments to study magnetic fields, solar wind, radiation, cosmic rays and micrometeoroids throughout its 7½-month flight through space to the planet Mars, but with a camera to photograph the Martian surface on the way past.

Mariner 4 was launched on November 28, 1964. Its initial trajectory would have taken it past Mars at a distance of 150,000 miles, but on December 5, in response to signals from Earth, it fired its built-in rocket motor to put it on a new course that would take it near enough for worthwhile photography. After that, it stayed on course by locking itself automatically on the sun and the bright star Canopus. On July 14–15, 1965, Mariner 4 successfully took the first close-up photographs of Mars. It recorded them on magnetic tape and transmitted them over a straight-line distance of 135 million miles, each picture being

Diagram showing the paths that Mariners 6 and 7 traced through space on their missions to Mars. Photographs were taken within 2,000 miles of the planet.

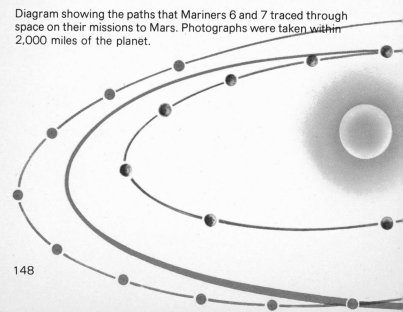

made up of some 40,000 dots in any one of sixty-four shades of light intensity between black and white. Strength of the signals picked up on Earth and converted into fine photographs was one ten-millionth, millionth, millionth of a watt!

Mariners 6 and 7 photographed Mars in July and August 1969. As the spacecraft approached the planet, cameras recorded the full disk of Mars. At close encounter within 2,000 miles, details 1,000 feet across were seen. Mars has the appearance of the moon, with craters covering a desolate landscape.

Soviet counterparts of Mariner are the one-ton Mars and Venus spacecraft. For several years these lacked success, most of them being lost through electronic shortcomings. Then, on March 1, 1966, Venus 3 crashed into the surface of the planet after which it was named. For the first time man had made physical contact with another planet. On October 18, 1967, Venus 4 approached the same planet and ejected an instrument-carrying capsule which was to have been soft-landed by parachute on the surface—a technique made possible by Venus's atmosphere. Unfortunately, high atmospheric pressure doomed the capsule before it reached the surface.

Soon, perhaps, close-up photographs of the surface of Mars, Venus and other planets and moons will be as familiar as the pictures of the Moon received in tens of thousands from Luna and Surveyor spacecraft.

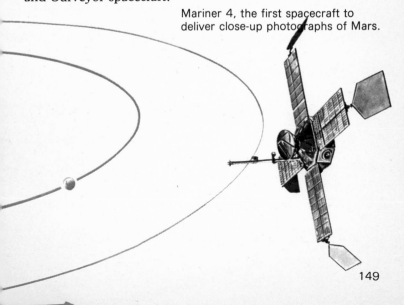

Mariner 4, the first spacecraft to deliver close-up photographs of Mars.

149

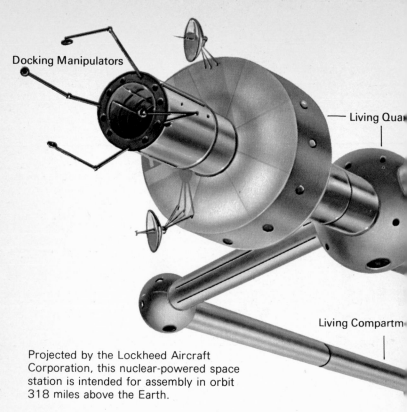

Docking Manipulators

Living Quar

Living Compartm

Projected by the Lockheed Aircraft
Corporation, this nuclear-powered space
station is intended for assembly in orbit
318 miles above the Earth.

Space station of the Future

As we have seen, the first orbital space stations will be simple
adaptations of existing spacecraft such as Saturn and Soyuz.
However, the docking techniques perfected by both the
United States and the Soviet Union already make it feasible to
construct very large orbiting laboratories by sending up the
components one at a time and assembling them in space.

Typical of the space stations that could be constructed in
this manner within the foreseeable future is this 200-ton design
by the Lockheed company. Measuring 108 feet long by 94 feet
wide, it is made up basically of spheres 18 feet in diameter and
cylinders 30 feet long by 10 feet in diameter. It would rotate
slowly to produce low artificial gravity and so make conditions
more comfortable for those working on board. Power for light-
ing, equipment and services would be provided normally by a
nuclear reactor, but there would also be a small piston-engine
for emergency power.

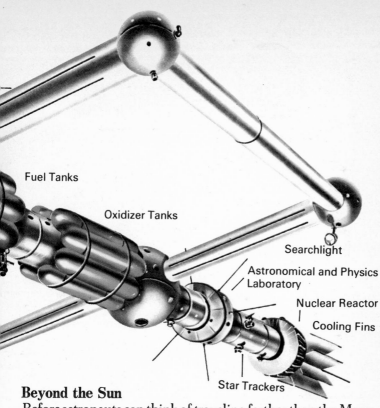

Fuel Tanks

Oxidizer Tanks

Searchlight

Astronomical and Physics
Laboratory

Nuclear Reactor

Cooling Fins

Star Trackers

Beyond the Sun

Before astronauts can think of traveling farther than the Moon, different types of rocket engine will be needed. The first ones will almost certainly be nuclear power plants. Primitive engines of this kind are already under test, promising immense power for long periods without the need for impractical quantities of propellents.

Several types of nuclear power plants are suitable for spacecraft. Simplest, perhaps, is that in which liquid hydrogen is fed into a nuclear reactor, which raises its temperature by thousands of degrees. The pure hydrogen gas is then ejected from a conventional kind of nozzle and the rocket is propelled forward.

Less developed than the nuclear power plant are the plasma jets, ion engines and other advanced concepts which may one day provide the propulsion needed for journeys into outer space. Then the high, short-lived power of the present-day

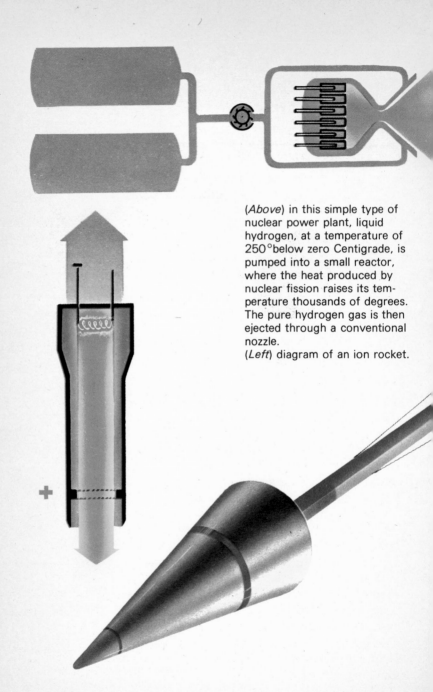

(*Above*) in this simple type of nuclear power plant, liquid hydrogen, at a temperature of 250°below zero Centigrade, is pumped into a small reactor, where the heat produced by nuclear fission raises its temperature thousands of degrees. The pure hydrogen gas is then ejected through a conventional nozzle.

(*Left*) diagram of an ion rocket.

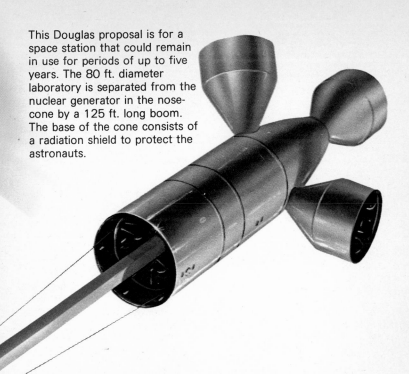

This Douglas proposal is for a space station that could remain in use for periods of up to five years. The 80 ft. diameter laboratory is separated from the nuclear generator in the nose-cone by a 125 ft. long boom. The base of the cone consists of a radiation shield to protect the astronauts.

rocket must give way to an engine that will offer a comparatively slow acceleration for very long periods of time.

A rocket that set out for the galaxy-of Andromeda, two million light-years from Earth, at a constant acceleration of 1 g would begin to approach the speed of light (670 million mph) after one year. At such speed strange things happen. In particular, time almost begins to stand still.

Even if a spacecraft traveled at the sort of speeds envisaged, our Earth would age by over five million years in the time taken for a return journey to the Andromeda galaxy, nearest other galaxy to our own; but an astronaut who made the trip might land only fifty-six years older than when he left. Einstein was the first to suggest that time slows down in this way when matter travels at the speed of light. It has since been proved during experiments in nuclear science; but one's mind boggles at the changes our astronaut of the distant future might find on returning as an old man to the home he left as a young man four million years earlier. . . .

All aboard the rocket-liner

Ion engines, plasma jets, journeys to Andromeda, even flights to the Moon, Mars and Venus, are not for us, the average men, women and children of the early 1970's. We have seen men on the Moon and may see supermen on the moons of other planets, in our lifetime; but even the other star systems of our own galaxy will remain mere twinkles in the sky; and we may never know whether or not all other bodies in the heavens are as desolate as the Moon and Mars.

For us, the supersonic airliners, cruising at much less than one-tenth orbital speed, seems a great and slightly unreal jump beyond the jetliners of today. Yet there is no reason why most of us could not have the opportunity of traveling in a rocket within twenty years—a shorter period than that which as elapsed since the first supersonic flight was made.

Rockets do not need to accelerate with a bone-crushing force that requires their occupants to be strapped horizontally to a contoured couch wearing a spacesuit. They do not need to encircle the entire globe or fly out into space before being of some practical use. And they do not have to cost millions of dollars per launch.

Already, engineers of the McDonnell Douglas Corporation, manufacturers of the DC-8 and DC-9 airliners as well as of the Mercury and Gemini spacecraft, have produced design studies of the kind of rocket in which ordinary people could travel safely and comfortably on everyday flights.

The original design, known as Pegasus, was for a vehicle 114 feet tall—a great metal craft shaped like a revolver bullet and surrounded at take-off by a ring of eight liquid-hydrogen tanks. On its four decks, 250 passengers could be carried from Los Angeles to Singapore in thirty-nine minutes, reaching a height of 125 nautical miles over the central Pacific. Los Angeles to Honolulu would take a mere eighteen minutes. Journeys to the most distant parts of the globe could be completed in forty-five minutes. An improved 'MK 2' version, called Hyperion, is illustrated opposite.

Just one word of warning. . . . Please do not address your requests for reservations on these services to the author—not just yet, anyway!

Hyperion on its way from
New York to London with 110
passengers on board, at a speed
of 17,000 mph. Instead of a seat,
each passenger would be allo-
cated a couch in the nose compartment. The biggest drawback would
be the fare, an estimated
three thousand dollars round trip.

BOOKS TO READ

View from a Height. Issac Asimov, Doubleday, 1963.

Voices from the Sky. Arthur C. Clarke. Harper & Row, 1965.

Rockets, Missiles and Space Travel. Willy Ley. Viking, 1957.

Express to the Stars. Homer E. Newell. McGraw-Hill, 1961.

Men of Space. (6 vols.). Shirley Thomas. Chilton, 1960–63.

This High Man. Milton Lehman. Farrar, Straus, 1963.

Space Flight. Carsbie Adams. McGraw-Hill, 1958.

Project Apollo. Thomas Alexander. Harper & Row, 1964.

V-2. Walter Dornberger. Viking, 1954.

Animal Astronauts. Clyde R. Bergwin and William T. Coleman. Prentice-Hall, 1963.

Interplanetary Flight. Arthur C. Clarke. Harper & Brothers, 1960.

Astronautics in the Sixties. Kenneth W. Gatland. John Wiley & Sons, 1962.

Sounding Rockets. Homer E. Newell. McGraw-Hill, 1959.

Basic Astronautics. Frederick Ordway, James Gardner and Mitchell Sharpe Jr. Prentice-Hall, 1962.

Space Flight Report to the Nation. (ed. J. and V. Grey). Basic Books.

Rockets and Spacecraft of the World. M. Chester. Norton.

Manned Spacecraft. Kenneth Gatland. Macmillan, 1967.

Space Pioneers. Willy Ley. Holt, Rinehart & Winston.

Space Rockets and Missiles. R. F. Yates and M. E. Russell. Holt, Rinehart & Winston.

Astronauts: The Story of Project Mercury. M. Caidin. Dutton.

Manned Space Flight. M. Faget. Holt, Rinehart & Winston.

Space Flight Dictionary. N. Roes. Follett.

Space Flight Encyclopedia. N. Roes. Follett.

Space Flight and How It Works. W. P. Gottlieb. Doubleday.

Space Flight: Countdown for the Future. E. Sanger (K. Frucht, ed.). McGraw-Hill.

History of Rocketry and Space Travel. Wernher Von Braun and Frederick Ordway. Crowell, 1967.

Rockets, Missiles and Space. V. Pizer. Lippincott.

INDEX

Page numbers in bold type refer to illustrations.

A-2 **79**
A-3 **20**, 22, **79**
A-4 22
A-9 38
AAP 132, **132**
Aerobee 78, 79
Agena 100, 106, **106**, 107, **107**
Air snatch 88, **89**
Air-to-air 41, **67**, 68–69
Air-to-surface 40, 41, 42–43, **44**, 45, 60
Alcohol 36, 79
Aldrin, Edwin 108, 128
Alouette **84**
An-22 **50**
Anab **67, 68**
Aniline 37
Anti-aircraft missile 40, 54, 56–59, 60
Anti-missile missle 29, 63
Anti-radar missile 43
Anti-submarine missle **70**
Anti-tank missile 31, 45, **45, 46,** 48–49
Apollo Applications Program *see* AAP
Apollo project 108, 119–129, 139
Armstrong, Neil 106, 128
Artillery missile **53**
Artillery rocket **30, 50**
AS-11 **44,** 45
AS-12 **42**
Asroc 70–71
Astronaut 96, **96,** 98, 103, 138
Atlas 29, **72,** 73–74, 80, 97, 98, 99, 122, **122**
Atlas-Agena 147
Atlas-Centaur 114

B-52 **40,** 41, 44, **44,** 134
Baikonur 102, 146
Ballistic Missle Early Warning System *see* BMEWS
Balloon 90, 91, **91**
Bazooka 31
Beam-riding guidance 59
Belyayev, Pavel 102
Black powder *see* Gunpowder
Bloodhound 57, **57**
Blowpipe **60,** 61
Blue Steel **41,** 42
BMEWS 63, **64,** 65
Boeing 142, **142** *see also* B-52
Bomber 40–42, **65**
Booster 73, 78, 83, 93
Borman, Frank 104
Boxer, Colonel 11, 12

Braun, Wernher von 20–22, 36, 81
BRDM **48,** 49, **49**
Britain 41, **41,** 42, **46,** 47, **57, 58,** 59, 61, **68,** 77, 137
Bullpup 43, **43**
Bykovsky, Valery 100

C-5A **50, 51**
C-130 **51,** 52
C-133 **50**
C-141A **50**
Cape Canaveral 96, **96**
Cape Kennedy 104, 114, 120, 124, 126, 146
Carcinotron 41
Carpenter, Scott 99
Cernan, Eugene 107
China 4, 63
Collins, Michael 107, **107,** 128
Command module 119, **119, 125, 126,** 129
Computer 37, 47, 56, 59, 70
Congreve, William 7, 8, 10
Conrad, Charles 104, 107
Control and guidance 28–77 *see* Radio control; Wire guidance
Cooper, Gordon 99, 104
Corporal **36,** 37, 50
Cosmonaut 95
Cosmos **89,** 109
Crusader **69**
Curtis *see* C-5A; C-130; C-133; C-141A

Decoy missile 29, 44, **44,** 45, 63, 77
Defense 65 *see* Anti-missile missile
Delta **65**
Deterrent 74–75
Do-217 27
Docking 106–109, 132
Dornberger, Walter 22
Dornier *see* Do-217

Early Bird **88**
Early warning *see* BMEWS
EC-135 75
EC-135C **74**
Egret 27
Eilat 34–35
Ejection seat 95, 100
Ente **18,** 20
Enzian **26**
Erebus 7, **7,** 8
Escape tower 99, 100, 119
Exhaust 28
Exocet 59
Explorer 81, 84–85

F-101B **69**
F-106 **65**

Falcon **68**
Feoktistov, Konstantin 100
Feuerlilie **27**
Fighter 65, 68, 69, **69**
Fire-arrow 4, 5
Firestreak **68**
Flying bomb **23,** 32–35, 40, 72
Fort McHenry 7, **7**
France 6, **42,** 45, 47, 59, **67, 69, 71,** 72, 77
Freedom 7 96, **97**
Friendship 7 98
Frezier **8,** 9, 11
FROG **30,** 31, **39**

Gagarin, Yuri Alekseyevich 92, **92,** 93, **93,** 95
Galaxy **51**
Galosh 63
Ganef 57, **57**
Ganswindt, Hermann 13
Gasoline 18, 21
Genie **67, 69**
Gemini project 100, **101,** 103, 104, 106, **106,** 107, **107,** 108, 130, **139**
Germany 16, 18–27, 25
Glenn, John 98, 99
Glushko, Valentin 18
Goddard, Robert 16–18
Gordon, Richard 107
Grissom, Virgil I. 97, 103
Ground attack weapons 42–44
Grumman 142, **142**
Guideline 56, **57,** 60
Gunpowder 4, 5, 8, 12, 13
Gyro stabilizer **17,** 33, 54

Hale, William **8,** 9
Hawk 60, **61**
H-bomb *see* Thermonuclear warhead
He-111 40
Heat shield 95, 99, 129
Heinkel *see* He-111
Hercules **51,** 52
HL-10 134, 135, **135**
Homing missile 40
Honest John **30,** 31, 61
Hound Dog **40,** 41
Hovercraft 55, **55**
Hs293 **24,** 26, 27
Hydrazine **103,** 141
Hyperion 154, **155**

ICBM 29, 38, **62,** 63, 73–74, **75,** 100, **101,** 122
Inertial guidance 32, 33, 36, 39, 42, 71, 73, 75
Infra-red homing 47, **67, 68,** 69
Integrated defense 65
Interceptor *see* Fighter

Intercontinental ballistic missile *see* ICBM
Intermediate-range ballistic missile *see* IRBM
Ion engine 151, **152**
IRBM 38

Japan **21**
Jet 35, **40**, 135
Jet-lift 13
Jupiter 38, 91

Katyusha **23**, 25, 31
Kennel **40**, 41
Kerosene 38, 124
Kibalchich, Nikolai **12**, 13
Komar patrol boat 35, **35**
Komarov, Vladimir 100

La Combattante 54
Laika 82–83, 90
Lance **50**
Launch tower **16**
Launcher 48–49, **50, 51**, 52, **53**, 55, 59, **60**, 70
Leonov, Aleksi 102
LFV 141, **141**, 143
Liberty Bell 7 97
Life support system **138**
Life-saving rockets 10–11, 12
Lightning **67**
Liquid hydrogen 14, 124, 132, 137, 143, 151, **152**
Liquid oxygen 14, 17, 18, 21, 36, 38, 49, 79, 124, 137, 143
Littlejohn **30**, 31
Long Beach 59
Lovell, James 104, 108
Luna 110, **110, 111**, 114, **115**
Lunar flying vehicle *see* LFV
Lunar module 119, **119, 126, 127**, 128, **132, 141**
Lunar orbiter 113, **113**

M2-F2 134, 135
Mace **32**, 33
Malafon **71**, 72
Manned Orbiting Laboratory *see* MOL
Mariner **146**, 147–149
Mars (planet) **146**, 147, 148, **148**
Mars (spacecraft) 149
Martel 43, **43**, 44
Matador 32, **32**, 33
Matra R-530 **67**
McDivitt, James 103
Me-163 **21, 26**
Me-262 **35**
Mercury project 36, 91, 92, 96, 97, 98, 99, **99, 122**
Messerschmidt *see* Me-163; Me-262
Micrometeroids 144, **145**
Minuteman 29, **29**, 74–75, **75**
Mirage **67**
Mirak **20**, 21
MOL 130, **131**, 145

Molab 142, **142, 143**
Molniya 87, **87**
Monkey 90, **90**, 96, 97
Moon 110–129
Moon landing 126–129
Multi-stage rocket 11–12, 14, **15**
Mustard 137, **137**

NASA 96, 97, 104, 111, 132
National Aeronautics and Space Administration *see* NASA
Natter **26**
Navy 54–55, 59, **68–71**, 76
Nike-Ajax 52, 56, **56**
Nikolayev, Andrian 100
Nimbus **89**
Nitric acid 37, 49
NORAD 65
Nord 47, 54
North American Air Defense Command *see* NORAD
Nuclear power 136, **150**, 151, **152, 153**
Nuclear warhead 31, 32, 35, 36, 38, 43, **58, 67**, 68, **69**, 71, 76, 83

OAO **87**, 88
Oberth, Hermann 16
Ohka **21**
Opel, Fritz von 18, **19**, 20
Orbital flight 92
Orbital workshop 132, **132**
Orbiting astronomical observatory *see* OAO
Orbiting solar observatory 133
Osa patrol boat 34

Parachute 95, 97, 99, 100, 129
Peenemünde 22
Pegasus 154
Pershing 50, **51**, 52
Phantom **68**
Pioneer 85, 110
Plasma jet 151
Pogo **140**
Polaris 35, 54, 70, 76, **76**
Popovich, Paval 100
Poseidon 77
Propellant, liquid 14, 17, 22, **27**, 29, **36**, 37, 38, 43, **43**, 49, 50, 52, 55, 56, 73, 78, 93, 119, 126
solid 17, 18, 28, 35, 43, 50, 52, 56, 59, 72, 74, 78, 117
Proton **88**
Pulsejet 24

Quail 44, **44**

R.530 **69**
Radar **37**, 40, 41, 56, 57, 59, 60, 61, **62**, 63, **64**, 65, 66, 68, 72, 79, 88
Radar homing 35, **67**, 69

Radio command guidance *see* Radio-control
Radio-control 26, 27, 33, 37, 43, 45
RAF **23, 57**
Ramjet 57, 59, 60
Ranger 111, **112**, 113
Rapier **60**, 61
Reaction 5, 14
Red Top **67, 68**
Redstone 36, **36**, 50, 81, 96
Re-entry 95, 99, 104, 129, 136
Regulus 35, 54
Rendezvous 104, 107, 132
Repulsor 21
Retro-rocket 100, 111, 116, **127**
Rheinbote 26
Rheintochter R-1 **24**
Rocket, history of 4–27
principle of 5, **5**
sounding 78, 79
space 78–91
Rocket aircraft **12**, 13, **19**, 20, **21**
see also Rocket-fighter
Rocket bomb **24**, 26
see also Flying bomb
Rocket car 18, **19**
Rocket sledge 20
Rocket-belt 140, **140**
Rocket-fighter **23**, 25
Rocket-liner 154
Roma 27
Royal Navy **68**, 77
Ruhrstahl SD-1400X 26
Ruhrstahl X-4 **25**

Safeguard **62**, 63
SAGE 65
Sagger **48**, 49
Sandal 39
Sander rocket 18, **19**, 20
Sasin **73**, 74
Satellite 16, 63, 73, 80, 82–87
military 88, **89**
weather 88, **89**
Satellite communications 86–87, **88**
Saturn I 123, **123**
Saturn V 14, 120–121, **122**, 123, 124–127, 132, 133, 145, **145**
Schirra, Walter 99, 104
Schmetterling **27**
Scott, David 106
Scrag **73**, 74
Scud **50**, 52
Sea Lance 55
Sea Vixen **68**
Seacat **58**, 59
Sergeant 50, **50, 53**
Seaslug 59
Semi-Automatic Ground Environment *see* SAGE
Service module 119, **119, 125**, 126, 129
Shepard, Alan B. 96, **96, 97**
Ship-to-ship 34
Shrike 43, 44

158

Shyster 38, **38**
Sidewinder **67**
Silo **28,** 74, **75**
Skean 39
SLOMAR 136
Snapper 48, 49
Snark 32
Solar cell 85, 116, **132**
Sonar 70, 72
Soyuz **118**
Space Logistics,
 Maintenance and Rescue
 see SLOMAR
Space station 130,
 150–153, **153**
Space travel 13, 14, 16, 82,
 92–132
Spacesuit 138–139
Space-taxi 136–137
Sparrow **68**
Spartan **62,** 63
Spin-stabilization 31, 47
Sprint **62,** 63
Sputnik 82–87, 91
SS-11 45, 47
SS-12 **46,** 47
SS-12M 54, **54,** 55
Stafford, Thomas 104, 107
Stand-off bomb 41
StarLifter **50**
Star-tracking guidance 32
Stick-rocket **9, 11**
Stratofortress **40,** 41
Styx 34, **34,** 35, **35,** 54
Submarine 70–72, 76–77
Sub-orbital flight 96, 98
Subroc **70,** 71
Super Constellation **64**

Super Guppy 120
Surface-to-air 41, 52, 56,
 59, 60
Surface-to-surface 54, **55**
Surveyor 114, **115,**
 116–117, 144
SV-5J 135
Swatter 49, **49**
Swingfire **46,** 47

Talos **58,** 59, 60
TCA **42, 46,** 47
Télécommande
 Automatique see TCA
Telstar 86, **86**
Tereshkova, Valentina 100
Terrier 59
Thor 38
Thor-Able 110
Thermonuclear warhead
 40, 41, 42, 73, 122
Thunderbird 57
Titan 29, **72,** 74, 100, **101,**
 103, 104, 130, **131**
Titov, Herman 100
Torpedo 71, 72
Transport aircraft 50–51,
 50–51
Tsander, Fridrikh 18
Tsiolkovsky, Konstantin
 Eduardovich 14, **145**
Tu-16 **40,** 41
Typhoon **23,** 25
Tyuratam **93**

V-1 **23,** 24, 40
V-2 22, **25,** 78
VAB 121

Van Allen, James 85
Vanguard 80–82
Venus (planet) **146,** 147,
 149
Venus (spacecraft) 149
Verein für Raumschiffahrt
 see VfR
Verne, Jules 16
Vernier motor 73, 93, 116
Vertical Assembly Building
 see VAB
VfR 20–21
Vietnam 56, 60
Vigilant **45, 46,** 47
Viking 79, 80
Voodoo **69**
Voshkod 100, 101, 102
Vostok 92, **92,** 93, **94,** 95,
 100, **122**
VTOL 13
Vulcan **41,** 42

Walking in space 102–103
Walleye 43, **43**
Wasserfall **27**
Weapon system 52
Weather forecasting 88
White, Edward 103
Wire-guidance **25, 42, 44,**
 45, **45, 46,** 47, 48, **48,** 54
World War I 16
World War II 22–27

X-23A **134**
X-24A 135

Yak-28 **68**
YF-12A **68**
Young, John 103, 107

OTHER TITLES IN THE SERIES

The GROSSET ALL-COLOR GUIDES provide a library of authoritative information for readers of all ages. Each comprehensive text with its specially designed illustrations yields a unique insight into a particular area of man's interests and culture.

NOW AVAILABLE

PREHISTORIC ANIMALS
BIRD BEHAVIOR
WILD CATS
FOSSIL MAN
PORCELAIN
MILITARY UNIFORMS, 1686–1918
BIRDS OF PREY
FLOWER ARRANGING
MICROSCOPES & MICROSCOPIC LIFE
THE PLANT KINGDOM
ROCKETS & MISSILES
FLAGS OF THE WORLD
ATOMIC ENERGY
WEATHER & WEATHER FORECASTING
TRAINS
SAILING SHIPS & SAILING CRAFT
ELECTRONICS
MYTHS & LEGENDS OF ANCIENT GREECE
CATS, HISTORY—CARE—BREEDS
DISCOVERY OF AFRICA
HORSES & PONIES
FISHES OF THE WORLD
ASTRONOMY
SNAKES OF THE WORLD
DOGS, SELECTION—CARE—TRAINING

SOON TO BE PUBLISHED

GUNS
EXPLORING THE PLANETS
DISCOVERY OF THE AMERICAN WEST
MAMMALS OF THE WORLD
ANIMALS OF AUSTRALIA & NEW ZEALAND
JEWELRY
WARSHIPS
TREES OF THE WORLD
COMPUTERS AT WORK
ARCHITECTURE
MONKEYS & APES
THE ANIMAL KINGDOM
DISCOVERY OF NORTH AMERICA
ENGLISH VICTORIANA
NATURAL HISTORY COLLECTING
MYTHS & LEGENDS OF ANCIENT EGYPT
THE HUMAN BODY
TROPICAL AQUARIUM FISHES
AFRICAN ANIMALS
VETERAN & VINTAGE CARS
MYTHS & LEGENDS OF THE SOUTH SEAS
MYTHS & LEGENDS OF ANCIENT ROME
MYTHS & LEGENDS OF ANCIENT INDIA
ARMS & ARMOR
DISCOVERY OF SOUTH AMERICA